60 MILES OF BAD ROAD

Thank-you to

God

for any small talent I may have – may You be
evident in all things.

Thank-you to my husband,

Jeff,

for encouragement – may I never forget that you
make life amazing – & that you kill spiders for me

This is for my children –

Jeni, Luke & Bendigo –

I love you all and you make life worthwhile –
may you have something of me when I'm gone.

And, for Josie... I still

ever

Annie ~

Mom says I started talking from the day I was born and never really shut up... I guess I always had a story to tell! And, I loved reading from the first day I learned a letter... I would read billboards, street signs, the backs of packages – almost anything with words. But, STORIES... those were my passion. And, reading authors like Louis L'Amour and Terry Brooks and Neil Gaiman and Rick Bragg and John Muir gave me a wide-ranging appreciation for all types of writers and stories. AND... made me uncomfortably aware of what really good writing is (especially Rick Bragg... what a magician with words he is...)

So... fair warning... I'm not them. BUT, I hope that these stories can bring you a small dose of the enjoyment that I find when reading my favorite authors.

AND.: that the recipes will not only fill your bellies, but perhaps give you a taste of my life also.

Thank you so much for visiting our little cafe. I hope you enjoy my stories & also have fun trying the recipes. See you @ the festival!
Jane Ashley

LIFE

Cooking up Memories 11

A Rocky Romance 15

The Headliners 19

Nabil-I 23

Snakes in a Bag 25

Mom.... Daughter 29

Wolf Pack 33

How To Kill A Grizzly With a Pam Can 35

Poem For Dad 45

BREAKFASTS & QUICK BREADS 47

_____Rhubarb Jam Coffee Cake 47

_____Brunch Egg Braid 48

_____Montana Banana Bread 50

MEAL STARTERS 51

_____Hamburger-Vegetable Soup 51

_____Tomato Bisque Soup 52

_____Mandarin Orange & Red Onion Salad 53

_____Winter Salad 54

_____Mustard Vinaigrette 54

_____Chicken Salad (for Sandwiches, Salads or Wraps) 55

_____Rustic Sourdough Bread (in a dutch oven) 56

_____Swope Bread 58

SIDE DISHES 59

_____Broccoli Puff....................................59

_____Herbed Red Potatoes.......................59

_____Herbed Corn....................................60

_____Butternut Squash.............................60

_____Pasta w/ Sundried Tomatoes & Bacon 61

ADAPTED FROM LIFE

Josie 65

Motherless Child...69

Sixty Miles of Bad Road 71

MAIN dISHES & CASSEROLES..........................81

_____Hereford Casserole 81

_____Pulled Pork......................................83

_____Baked Pork Chops 84

DESSERTS..85

_____Zucchini – Chocolate Cookies 85

_____Strawberry Rhubarb Pie...................86

_____Cowboy Cookies...............................87

_____Old-Fashioned Bread Pudding w/ Rum Sauce 88

_____Pecan Tassies 90

_____Beet Cake 91

_____Peach Cobbler..................................92

SAUCES, MARINADES & MISC...93

_____Sweet / Spicy Marinade for Flank Steak 93

_____Chimichurri Sauce (for red meats)..............................93

_____Jezebel Sauce (for pork and white meats)................93

FANTASY LIFE

Annabelle...97

Belle's of Freedom..105

Baggage 131

LIFE

COOKING UP MEMORIES

In the corner stands an ancient corner hutch. Made of pine and with the patina of age, I rescued this dubious treasure from a crumbling wreck of what was once a proud pioneer home.

In the hutch, a small triangular shelf holds what passes for my collection of kitchen recipes, hints and manuals. Regardless of the wide variety of small recipe collections that I insist on toting home from every 4-H display, church potluck and Firehouse feed, I faithfully return to the one and only Betty Crocker cookbook, which evokes with every meal, fond memories of my formative years.

Unknown to me as a child, my mother was that rarest of souls in 1942 when my father brought her home as his wife – a female who didn't know the basics of cooking. Betty Crocker was her best friend in the kitchen during those early days. It wasn't until my second marriage and third child that I, too, discovered this treasure. Browsing the meager selection of the local bookstore, I happened across a familiar cover that suddenly reminded me of a similar one which my mother stored on a small kitchen shelf of her own. Since then my entire family has enjoyed the traditional tastes of the home-cooked meals, which remind us all of the comforting dinners and cozy evenings spent in her kitchen.

Next to the Betty Crocker is a battered and ragged spiral photo album. Gracing its cover is an expectant gray kitten posing prettily in a psychedelic display of flowers, ala 1972. Cleverly disguised by this charming sight, is a collection of recipes, meticulously clipped from The Daily Interlake over the course of many years. As far as I can remember, we never sampled any of these apparently alluring concoctions. However, it is reassuring to realize that my penchant for collecting recipes I will never actually prepare is genetic, rather than some as yet un-named psychological condition for which I'll require numerous sessions with a professional who specializes in recovery from "an addiction to useless collections".

However, the most beloved, although unexpected, resident of this shelf, is the recipe card box. Casually tucked into a cardboard box containing other equally practical items, the recipe cards in THIS little metal chest conjure feelings generally only experienced with a perusal of the cedar chest in which Mother kept her mementos and keepsakes.

While some, like "Strawberry Chocolate Delight" are on vintage recipe cards printed by Rosauers Grocery Store, and others have been carefully cut from newspapers, the ones that I truly cherish are handwritten in Mother's precise and clearly identifiable script, or typed on blank cards for better longevity. Stained, folded, footnoted – these collected recipes combine in a seemingly random and untidy manner that ultimately results in a deep and rich experience – just like her Crazy Cake recipe.

I slowly leaf through the sections, stopping here and there to pull out a particularly tasty sounding title, or to gaze at "Gram's Fruit Cake from Eunice" – wondering if it's actually good fruit cake (I don't remember her ever actually enjoying fruit cake...), or if she wanted it because it came from her sister. But, the one I most enjoy pulling from the little box, is one with no title but is obviously for potato rolls. Not because of the recipe itself, but because of what it's written on – an envelope with a 3cent stamp, mailed from Minnesota in 1957 and addressed to my namesake – Mrs. Sarah Connell in North Dakota. I wonder... who lived in Minnesota? And what was in the little envelope? And how did my Mother, in Montana, end up with it? And who gave her the recipe on the back?

As I ponder, I wonder... will my descendants cherish my odd collection of index cards, books, and binders in which I keep both my recipes – and those from my own parents? Or, will the easy availability of recipes and online reviews in today's world make the kitchen recipe collection a thing of the past? Will they pull out the little envelope and remember who Sarah Connell was – and who I was? Will we have cooked up enough Memories to withstand the ravages of time and distance? Or, will we all become just a faint scrawl on an old envelope in their mind.

A ROCKY ROMANCE

Do you remember those Pepe LePeu cartoons? How devoted the little lovesick skunk was to the bewildered object of his affections? Well, this is a true story of unrequited love between two very different species.

Hot as a smoking barrel and dry as gunpowder, the weather that fall had conspired to keep the rut slow and relatively inactive there in the backcountry of Montana's Bob Marshall Wilderness. The desultory attitude of the antlered participants made Jeff's job as a guide unusually difficult.

As Jeff and his fellow guide, Scott, rose in the wee hours of that auspicious day, they had no inkling that they would be given the privilege of participating in that most impressive of rituals, the Bull Elk Mating Dance.

Four hunters from "back east" had journeyed to the West, to hunt the wily Wapiti in "The Bob" as locals referred to the rugged wilderness just south of Glacier National Park. Four days of the eight-day hunt had already passed with nary a bull sighted. For lack of a better plan, Jeff and Scott determined to combine forces that day and take all four hunters up the Trickle Creek drainage which would offer a slightly easier hunt than previous days, while still allowing all four dudes a group hunt.

At daylight, with the hunters sitting gingerly in their saddles, six horses picked their way up the rocky trail. Two hours on horseback brought the group to the dismounting site just below the forested portion of the drainage. Knowing that cooler temperatures offered by the trees would be a preferred spot for elk in the pressing heat, it was decided to split up and send two hunters around each edge and meet at the head, effectively "putting the squeeze" on any elk in the timber. The availability of water, shelter, shade and wallows in the trees would require the men to pressure the elk closely before any of the creatures would move, thereby offering a shot.

However, upon hearing the plan, the hunters maintained that it was too much effort and requested that the guide's squeeze the elk while they, the hunters, waited below for the game to show. Jeff and Scott explained the un-likelihood of elk running <u>down</u> the mountain right into their laps, but the hunters remained adamant. So, bowing to their client's wishes, the piqued guides headed up into the timber.

Preceding Jeff by a few yards, Scott bugled every few steps but with little expectation of a response. After 200 yards, the terrain became brushy and thick. As the two men were tromping their way through this obstacle course, they nearly fell over when an answering squeal was heard just ahead. Now, admittedly, it was a very poor excuse for a bugle, but still... it was a <u>bull</u>! Quitting the bugle, Scott started cow-talking, answering each pitiful squeal with a "come-hither" she-elk grunt. At the same time, the guides stepped into a small clearing and took the opportunity to try & locate Romeo.

Suddenly, hooves sounded - on a collision course with the two surprised guides. "Holy S---" exclaimed Scott.....It's trotting right to us!!" Antler tips bobbed above the brush like pinecones traveling down a stream. Never slowing, the expectant elk burst into the clearing only to be greeted by these two strange looking cows. Undaunted, the regal 5x5 bull paraded at a trot for the two appreciative guides. Back and forth across the meadow, like a plastic duck in a shooting gallery, he exhibited his attributes, never once pausing to question his audience. His panting and slobbering were accompanied by mewing, grunting and other displays too risqué for further explanation. The lonely lovesick bachelor was too keyed up to even bugle correctly. Each trumpet ended up sounding more like a bath toy than the challenging mating call of a forest prince.

While enjoying the show, the two guides quietly debated the feasibility of Jeff slipping away to bring back a hunter. However, just as it was agreed that an attempt should be made, the elk crossed a nearby brook, picked up their scent and trotted directly away while still bleating pitifully as if hoping he was wrong about the very UN-appealing man-scent.

With the departure of the love-sick target, the guides again briefly considered that they go down and bring a hunter up to trail the elk, but the hunters' earlier unwillingness to exert themselves for the hunt decided the guides on a different course. So, up the drainage they continued. The lovesick elk had apparently gone in search of more amenable company, although Scott maintains that he could hear the creature following them all afternoon, like a lonesome puppy.

After a short lunch break just short of the crest, during which they watched a trophy size black bear forage in a nearby clearing, the guides continued on around the drainage intending to work their way back to their hunters. A muley-buck changed their plans once again, however. Stalking to within 75 yards, Scott and Jeff drooled over the old mossy-horned buck. The Boon and Crockett-sized, double-drop tine patriarch browsed unconcernedly among the boulders at the rock crest.

As evening settled its royal mantle around the peaks, the weary but contented guides slowly wandered back down the mountain. When queried by the well-rested hunters as to whether they expected the next day to provide any better hunting, Jeff and Scott replied - "Oh, not unless we run into a love-sick elk-sized bath toy".

THE HEADLINERS

Bandoliers. Crossed Bandoliers. Crossed Bandoliers Filled With Shells. She blinked slowly. They were still there. As she raised her eyes to those of the game warden who'd knocked on her door, he rumbled, "We have received a report of poached venison at this residence."

As confusion was replaced with shock, she tucked her chin and croaked, "Excuse me?"

"We have a search warrant authorizing a search of these premises for illegal bounty," she heard dimly in her shocked state. Her four scared, yet curious children crowded behind her, peeking wide-eyed at the imposing officer in his black logger jeans and blue chambray shirt. He cradled his shotgun in one arm while a rather large pistol resided threateningly on his hip.

"Who's that Mom?" the oldest asked.

"What's he want?" queried another. The youngest, Susan, popped her thumb into her mouth and hid behind Mom. They all stared in astonishment at the big dogs being led toward them by the warden's sidekick. The little group parted like the Red Sea for Moses, as the hounds pulled their handler into the cabin. The sniffers began their quest for that elusive venison smell they were so well-trained in hunting down.

As each nook and cranny was thoroughly inspected, Guin was vaguely aware of the dry breeze ruffling the white curtains at each window. The hot August day had seemed benign until now. Gerry, his nose stuck in a book since early morning hadn't been seen until the rap on the door offered. Karen and Connie were undoubtedly off brewing mischief, while Susan toddled around following Mom.

However, the sudden intrusion by the deer patrol livened things up quickly. Gerry found more stimulating – and realistic – fare than the book in his lap. Karen and Connie enjoyed the unexpected excitement, but Susan refused to budge from behind Mom's skirts.

After tracking dirt into every corner, the persistent duo removed their search party to the outbuildings where, again, their hands turned up venisonless. Retreating to their pickup, they muttered between themselves about "poachers " and "hiding places".

As Guin's mind resumed rational thinking, she slowly realized what had likely initiated the bizarre afternoon. The neighbor's son, Einar, had raised a pet goat. After concluding it was becoming too wild (the escape artist particularly loved the neighbor's flowers... ALL the neighbors' flowers) his parents asked Don and Guin if they could use it. As income, and by extension, groceries, were scarce, it was butchered and hung in a shed. A local good Samaritan spied the hanging meat and dutifully reported that the Bellers were poaching deer. However, by the time it was investigated, the goat had been removed to Vandevanter's for processing and then tucked into a meat locker.

When the over-eager Fish and Game officers figured out about the locker, they rushed down to Vandevanter's while congratulating each other on their poacher-catching prowess. Triumphantly, they peeled the white butcher paper away, revealing the very gray goat meat. Amazingly uneducated for game wardens, the two officers were already planning their spectacular arrest of Don. To their chagrin, Gene Vandevanter spoke up. "You two might be game wardens, but you sure don' t know your meat " he proclaimed quietly.

The following day, Mel Ruder headlined the escapade in his paper, the Hungry Horse News. "Local Citizen Gets Game Warden's Goat" read the caption. As the silly incident became common knowledge and the source of immense amusement at the expense of the wardens, Don and Guin felt fully compensated for the officers' ill-mannered, and un-warranted, intrusion.

NABIL-I

"Directions are on the handle," Dad said as he handed me the reins. The blue-roan gelding quivered slightly as I gently gathered up the slack in the split leather reins and sat lightly waiting for him to relax. Dad stepped away and his glance was seemingly casual as we both anticipated the many responses the gelding could choose.

Having come to us abused and neglected, Nabil-I was the embodiment of my father's heart. Big, strong and passionate, the horse was a *sharp contrast* to the malnourished spooky and sick four-year-old that Dad had led home six months earlier after a visit to one of his charges. As an AA sponsor, Dad had dealt with the best and worst of humanity all in the lowest of situations. This time, a young family, who'd lost everything, were living on beans, rice, and water. The baby was in only slightly better condition than the young horse in the pasture outside. With every cent going to try and feed his family, the man had no spare funds to purchase feed for the horse. The starving gelding had resorted to eating pine bark and dirt. Its head had begun to grow around the yearling halter which had never been removed, as if it was being slowly absorbed. But even so, the fierce spark of its proud Arabian heritage still glinted from deep inside his slowly dulling eye.

Completely disabled from his own Rheumatoid Arthritis, Dad was unable to work and so our own situation was scarcely more stable. But, the pride in the gelding's bearing found a mate within the man's soul. And, the pity in his heart cried out at the abject poverty of the family. So, giving our last $400 for the gelding, Dad gave them a small step up in their agonizing battle and gave the young horse a new start in life.

Now, after gaining hundreds of pounds and gallons of attitude, Nabil-I was poised to take the next step in his training program. Clucking firmly, I gently nudged his sides with my heels and lifted the reins. The gelding tensed briefly and rolled his eyes as if trying to determine what form of action was called for. After the quick survey, I felt the release of his tension as he relaxed and stepped forward as directed by my wishes being transmitted down the handles.

SNAKES IN A BAG

It wasn't my favorite spot, but the south fork still had its attractions. That particular day, the excitement was in the form of dozens of baby snakes. Kathie and I discovered the nest in the lee of an overhanging bank at the edge of the south fork of the Flathead River. We were camped at the far end of the same canyon where my parents had camped as they were growing up. Now, however, the canyon was the home of the reservoir held in place by Hungry Horse Dam.

At two years my junior, my niece Kathie was my closest companion. Her fair hair and bright blue eyes were a perfect foil for my darker mane and mud brown orbs. We were well-matched in height as well. While her willowy limbs could reach the areas far above my head, my short stature allowed access to the little niches otherwise inaccessible. We were a good team. A dangerous team – as illustrated by our antics that July afternoon.

Scampering into camp, Kat and I tripped over each other's words. "Grandma?" "Mom?" we chorused. "We need a sack!" "Yeah – a PAPER bag" Kat emphasized.

"What on earth do you need a sack for?" we were queried by Mom/Grandma.

"Oh…. Well…. " I began.

"We want to COLLECT stuff" Kathie improvised.

"YEAH! NEAT stuff!" I volunteered.

Shooting us both a cautious, perhaps suspicious look, Mom directed us to the camper where the used grocery bags were stowed. Armed with our tools – a Butter's paper bag and a forked stick – we scurried back to the squirming den of black offspring.

After carefully picking up the slithering mass and deposited it intact in the bag, we stopped to confer about our next move. "These are SO cool. Let's take them back to camp to show everyone!" I enthused.

"Grandma would LOVE them. She's always showing us neat stuff!" Kathie agreed.

Knowing Mom's... dislike of snakes, I wasn't so sure. But, with the expectation of an enthusiastic response of any sort, I gladly trotted along behind as Kat bolted back to camp. Handing the brown sack with the top folded over to Mom, Kathie was near quivering with excitement. "We brought you something, Grandma!" she exclaimed.

"What is it?" Mom was eyeing the sack warily.

"A present! We found it!" Kat declared proudly. I edged cautiously out of the danger zone as Mom unrolled the top and peered inside. But, she gave no response. Didn't she see them? Was I mistaken in her hate of them? Then I saw the blood drain from her face and her eyes grow large. For a moment, the entire scene was frozen. Mom at the center, eyes transfixed inside the bag. Kathie facing her, with expectant eyes and clasped hands. Karen, my sister and Kathie's mom, to the side, giving mom a puzzled look. And I – I was inching backward, prepared to flee for my life.

Then the frozen moment snapped and the explosion began. Mom's mouth slid open and a thin sound started out. Her eyes slowly sought mine and I spied the anger that can only be stoked by a deep fear, vying with shock in her face. As the full shriek emerged and expelled her initial fright, the words started. "OH MY GOD!" She dropped the sack.

"They're babies!" Kat explained. "What's wrong?" She didn't immediately understand what was happening. "Oh, you little MONSTERS!" Mom screeched. Having fulfilled my every expectation and more, I began laughing. I'd known she didn't like snakes, but I never expected her to come quite so unglued. Not my stoic, emotionally guarded mother! The sight of her jumping straight up and back away from the "gift" while sputtering retribution threats, screeches and gibberish in one continual steam, was more than I could take in. I laughed so hard that my stomach hurt.

In the meantime, Kat was scrambling to pick up the sack and save "the babies", while darting scared and puzzled glances at her raving grandmother and stuttering phrases to her mom. "I didn't know… What's wrong… I didn't mean….".

And then as one, they looked at me - the only one NOT shouting and scrambling. Upon realizing my danger, I turned and fled, Kathie at my heels. "SARA!!!" I heard Mom's and Karen's irate tones following, promising severe penalties upon my eventual return.

MOM

(I wrote this first short piece the same day it occurred. The 2nd short piece, written from Mom's perspective, was written many years later)

Meals are the hardest time. The rest of the day can, at times, feel almost normal – if normal is peering close into her hazel eyes to talk, mere inches from her age-lined face. Or, focusing on straightening her room in a vain effort to ignore the smell of illness and age. Even discussing with the nurse the short future she has left is "expected". But what isn't expected, is the stab of grief that pierces my fragile shell as I spoon pureed fish into my Mother's mouth. Sorrow mingled with a warped humor assails me as I realize I'm pursing my own lips and opening them as I encourage her to open for the bite. The image of feeding my babies in the same manner and the knowledge that she once fed me the same way, is the obvious picture that flashes like a still from an old black and white movie. But, what pierces me the most, is the memory of the strong-willed, independent, opinionated and active woman that she once was – as compared with this fragile and compliant shell of the mother I remember.

Having lived with the paralysis of her lower extremities for over twenty years, she had yet retained her fierce independence and energy levels. But, last year, diagnosed with a new disease, she was denied even the illusion of mobility and independence. The disease has taken her ability to interact in any meaningful way. The muscles of her face, neck, and shoulder are nearly paralyzed, resulting in mostly those expressions that are reflexive, not intentional. Now, wholly dependent on others for her sustenance, movement, cleanliness and all care, the one thing she retains is her stoic disposition and innate dignity. Never one to complain about unalterable facts, she still accepts her lot and awaits the near end with what little humor and grace can yet be expressed.

And, so, I tease her gently about her loud or difficult daughters and her slow and muffled answers show her determination to remain herself. "I'm going to sit with you awhile Mom," I say directly into her half-closed eyes. "I'll try to be quiet. – You know how quiet I am anyway." I smile at her.

"You? Quiet? Don't think so" she retorts slowly.

"Well, at least I'm not the difficult one!" I laugh.

"Yeah, right!" is the long-running and expected retort she offers.

For now, she's still my Mom, even with the feeding and funny mouth faces I make. I straighten her room and ignore the smell and sounds of the nursing home – and refuse to look ahead when she can no longer spar with words or teach me dignity with silence.

DAUGHTER

I've learned patience ~ or rather had it forced upon my limbs. Haste, frustration, anger - all seemingly cut from my psyche as the feeling was cut from my legs. Or at least that's the image I portray to those around me. But, at least I still had my mind, words, expressions with which to interact with others. Now, even that is being stripped from me. My face a frozen mask, neck stiff and rigid, my tongue a lump. I can see the pity and fear and hurt in my daughters' when they lean close so that I can see them through my hardening eye.

Sara purses her lips and then opens them, in the bird motion, encouraging me to eat as I once did her. Finally, unwilling to be spoon-fed any more today, I force my heavy lids and rock lips closed, signaling my completion.

WOLF PACK

The weather had been playing it's favorite bait-&-switch game all day. Earlier, great gusts of snow-laden wind had suddenly darkened the ranch yard where moments before bluebirds had been cavorting in the sun. Now, the snow had momentarily turned to a cold mist that lightened the surrounding hills.

A long echoing howl floated down, followed and then overtaken by melodic harmonies alternately holding a note and then fading, just to have another take its place with a yip and chittering yowl.

Rushing to the spotting scope, I beheld my first sighting of a Frank Church wolf pack. Sitting perfectly and spaced as precisely as if choreographed, the ten wolves were surveying the lower kingdom from their perch on a high crest. The light snow falling at that elevation softened their outlines through the scope, but the details were still evident. Nine gray with black members arrayed themselves around one monstrous white wolf, sitting off-center in the pack.

As I watched, the white wolf lifted it's muzzle to the side and formed a perfect "O". Immediately, several other mimicked the motion. Seconds later their brief serenade drifted to my wondering ears again.

Then, within moments, a decision was made with no visible sign. The pack rose & turned left and disappeared as a unit over the crest. But, as if to tantalize, a few reappeared briefly, then they too faded into the darkening eve and let the snow cover their tracks.

HOW TO KILL A GRIZZLY WITH A PAM CAN

"Jeff. Jeff!! There's something in the garbage can!" I shook his arm as I listened to the banging and grunting.

"So??" He grouched. "Get rid of it!" He obviously wasn't grasping the seriousness of the issue. Of course, that might be because just two nights earlier I'd declared the same thing.....

———

The noise, seemingly right next to my head, jolted me awake. There it was again – a loud screeching, scratching noise. Anything that made THAT noise had some CLAWS! I shook Jeff. "Hey. HEY... there's something under the bed!"

It had long been a source of contention that, apparently, there are NO night sounds in his world. Since his hearing had gone to pot, and at night with his "good" ear (a term used loosely at best) against the pillow, he was seldom awoken by any sound (including my snoring so that was a plus). As usual, he mumbled a grouchy "Whaat?" to which I replied, "There's something under the BED!".

He sat up for one second and then flopped back down. "There's nothing under the bed" he derided, since apparently if he can't hear it, it doesn't exist.

I listened another moment – "There it is again!" I demanded.

"Then get up & see what it is" he grumbled.

I crept carefully out of bed, turned on the light and tiptoed back to the bedside. Suddenly I heard it again "Screeeeccch" from the plastic garbage can by the bed. I very carefully peeked inside – nothing moved. I slowly lifted the sack out – still nothing. "Huh, must have ran off" I figured silently. I turned out the light & crawled back in bed, just in time for the talons to once again scratch their hideous sound. Jumping up and again turning on the light, I also grabbed a flashlight to shine down in the can. For the second time I carefully lifted the sack out of the can. And there, staring back at me was the cutest little gray field mouse with, apparently, claws the size of forks. His color exactly matched the can so he blended in quite well when not moving which explained how I'd missed him the first time. I cautiously carried the bin to the back door & let him go on his way.

———

So, this night, Jeff logically assumed that we had another little gray visitor and was quite miffed at me waking him up for such an inconsequential issue. But I was quite certain that this time, the noisy critter was a fair amount larger than our recent interloper.

"No! I think it's a BEAR" I whispered as I sat up & listened to the grunting & banging outside the house.

"Then go look." He wasn't convinced & wasn't getting up if I was wrong. So, against my better judgement, I crawled quietly out of bed & put on my robe. Tiptoeing to the side door of the cabin, I cautiously opened it, stuck my head out and peeked down the side the house. There at the corner, just ten feet away and gloriously lit up by the moon, was a very large and noisy grizzly bear ripping at some garbage and jumping on the 35 gallon drum we'd had it stored in, (and right next to the wall on the side of which Bendigo was sleeping the sleep of the innocent). Apparently hearing me, regardless of my caution, he stopped his jumping, turned his head and stared back at me as if to say "What are YOU looking at?? I shut the door.

Back in the bedroom, I shook Jeff awake again. "There's a grizzly in the garbage!"

Knowing that I wasn't going to let it go until he got up, he reluctantly rose and went to the side door, where, after having his own stare-down with the grizzly – he shut the door.

Now, letting a grizzly think he can have his way with your garbage is never a great idea – even if it's true (I mean, who in their right mind actually argues with a griz?) So, whenever possible, it's important to at least try to bluff them into thinking it's a bad idea. Based on this theory, we'd recently been given both "cracker" shells and rubber bullets by the local Montana Fish Wildlife & Parks bear biologist "just in case" something like this scenario arose. So, Jeff got his shotgun, loaded it with cracker shells, carefully opened the door and aiming over the bear's head, discharged the shot. Mr. Griz shook his head a little & continued with his feast. So, figuring we needed to bump up the annoyance level, Jeff loaded the rubber slugs and again eased open the door. Sighting in on the oversize rump, he once again let the bear have it.

This time he got a definite response. The bear roared and spun around, standing up to try & get a better look at whatever stung him. But, while he was a lot angrier, he was NOT any more inclined to leave his tasty buffet. So, Jeff shut the door & said "He can have the garbage" and returning to bed, quickly returned to his gentle sleep. Turning out the light, I also laid back down — and proceeded to listen to the sounds of the massive bruin enjoying his easy meal for several hours. And, wondering how Bendigo had missed all the ruckus, including the shotgun, as his head was a on a pillow just inches from where the bear was carrying on. Only one, very solid (fortunately) cabin log was between he & the bear.

In the morning, we carefully forayed out to see what damage our nighttime visitor had wrought. As we started raking up the mess, we found an exploded Pam pan spray can with blood on it. Seeing this, we assumed that the bear had bitten into it causing it to explode. It apparently kinda ticked him off when it exploded in his mouth as he had expressed his displeasure by leaving large toothmarks on one of the house logs, along with more blood.

While we'd never left much garbage outside and never for very long, after that night, it became taboo to leave ANY garbage or other attractant outside, even temporarily. And, while we didn't see him anymore that fall, a year later we again began having trouble.

As per his usual morning routine, Jeff was pacing the perimeter of the house, looking out each window to see what might have changed overnight, or what critters might be loitering, or what horses might be out of their assigned quarters. As he looked down at the barn, he did a double take. "Why's the barn door open?!" he exclaimed. It was a hard and fast rule that the door was always closed over night to prevent unwanted visitors. Presuming someone had forgotten that rule, he got dressed and wandered down to shut it before crew breakfast was served in the crew room of the lodge. As he neared the big double sliding plank doors, he realized something was amiss. The door hadn't been left open – it had been LIFTED off its track and set aside. Passing into the dark interior, he poked his head into the "grain" room – an area to the side where any horse feed that might attract attention was stored in old chest freezers. To his surprise, one end of the largest freezer had been peeled down like a banana! And, the culprit had eaten his fill of the grain stored inside before wandering off.

After breakfast, while the wranglers toted all the grain to the barn loft where it would, hopefully, be safe from the marauder, Jeff called Montana Fish & Wildlife bear biologist Kevin Fry. According to Kevin, the ranch down the road had been having issues for several weeks with a grizzly that had been causing havoc at their barn as well, and he assumed that it had just moved five miles up the road to our barn after electric fencing and other bear-deterrent measures had been implemented. He assured Jeff that he'd be out with a bear-trap, although he didn't expect to actually CATCH the bear based on previous encounters.

True to his word, he arrived later that afternoon with the trap, some bait and a trail camera to set up so he could get pictures of the bear to verify which one it might be. After getting the trap set, he instructed everyone to stay away from it and if anyone noticed that it had been triggered (the door closed) to NOT go near it and for Jeff to call him & he'd come right out.

During his window rounds early the next morning, Jeff noticed that, indeed, the trap had been triggered. He called Kevin to let him know and then promptly wandered down to the barn to see if the bear had actually been captured. As he walked cautiously up to the trap, he was aware of the deep quiet. Staying well back, he tiptoed around the back and looked through the grated door.... No bear.

Once Kevin arrived, he hooked the trail cam up to his laptop to see if the bear had visited overnight. Sure enough, the big bruin had been the star of the photos – and he knew it. The pictures clearly showed him as he wandered up to the trap, sniffing at the deer carcass hanging inside as bait. As he shuffled by the camera, he turned his head and stared directly at it so that everyone could get a good look at his seemingly amused gaze. Then, he paced around the trap and peeked in both ends at the "easy" meal just hanging there. But, older and wiser than many other bears, he knew a trap when he saw one. Returning to the rear, he wrapped his oversize paws around the edge and shook it until the gate finally dropped. Returning to the front, he carefully slid his big mitt inside and grasped the deer carcass with his claws. Jerking back, he yanked and pulled until he shredded it through the grilled window. As he made off with his prize, he once more stopped and stared at the camera in apparent disdain for our poor human attempt at catching him.

Assuring us that it was definitely an old boar that he'd run into in the past, Kevin reset the trap but with little hope that our nighttime visitor would be caught. After several more nights with no more excitement, he was proven correct, and we went into winter wondering where the old grizzly had wandered off to for his winter nap. According to Kevin, he had appeared severely underweight and that was probably part of why he'd been such a nuisance that fall, and that he may not hibernate as deeply nor as long as would be typical as he'd probably need a mid-winter break to restock his fat supplies.

The winter passed uneventfully as we went about our snow-season projects of repair & replace, answer phones and generally recover from the busy summer and fall seasons. And, as they always do, the warm sunlit days rolled around once again. My regular afternoon rides were once again a wonderful break from the long days in the kitchen and I started enjoying exploring new nooks and crannies in the mountains around us. Of particular interest were the hills just to the north of the ranch, where a beautiful little lake nestled just behind Lincoln mountain. I would ride the loop around the mountain, passing by the lake and on back to the ranch often, as it was almost exactly two hours. But, on the days I had more time, I'd venture off the trail and further up to see what might be just out of sight. One day in early July, I was taking just such a detour into a new area that looked promising. As I crested over a little hill, with the lake to my back, I was astonished to see what I would later come to call "The Killing Fields". Bones were scattered everywhere I looked. Thousands of them in the small, two-acre bowl. I rode slowly through the grass eyeing what was obviously the front yard of a wolf den. They must have had a LOT of pups to feed... I was shocked at the number of carcasses that had been drug home. Due to the sheer volume of bones, there wasn't any clear way to evaluate the carnage. But, by counting skulls as I found them, I came up with the following tally: 24 Deer, 12 elk, 1 moose, a beaver and countless birds. AND... most surprising – one giant grizzly skull. With a shattered canine tooth.

And that's the story of how I killed a grizzly with a Pam can.

POEM FOR DAD

I remember crossing rivers on shoulder
High above the swiftly running waters
And coming out each trial's other side
Because I had you as my loving father

I remember "directions are on the handle"
And that I have to hold my mouth just right
Because things may not always go my way
And, it's far too easy to lose this fight

I remember how you were ever a friend
of Bill W's, and every man on the street
How you taught me all people are precious
And that you carried your pride with humility

I remember how you seemed as large
and as solid as an old oak tree,
And yet were always soft as butter
When it came to caring for me

I remember hands - large as dinner plates,
and a personality to match.
But it's not your shoes I strive to fill,
It's the size of your heart, I long to have.

I remember you singing Amazing Grace
Why Me Lord and How Great Thou Art
And How you weren't afraid to love Jesus
Left a quiet, but indelible mark.

I remember you mimicking big black crows
And watching clouds with me on summer days
You taught me driving and whistling   and faith
And to always and ever to go my own way.

I'll remember all of these things always
And every day, I miss you more
Than I did all of last year and
The year before, and before, and before.

BREAKFASTS & QUICK BREADS

Rhubarb Jam Coffee Cake

Because you asked for it – Jan Bonn

Ingredients:

Cake:
- 1 ½ c. Flour
- ½ c. Sugar
- 2 tsp Baking Powder
- ½ tsp Baking Soda
- 2 tsp Cinnamon
- ½ tsp Salt
- 1 c. Rhubarb Jam
- 2/3 c. Buttermilk

- 1 Egg
- 1 tsp. Vanilla

Topping:
- ¾ c. Flour
- ¾ c. Brown Sugar
- 1 ½ tsp Cinnamon
- 6 TB Butter, softened

Directions:

1. Preheat oven to 350°F F. Spray loaf pan with non-stick cooking spray or line with parchment paper.
2. Make topping by rubbing flour, sugar & spice into the flour until crumbly.
3. Whisk together dry ingredients. Add jam, milk & egg, stir until combined.
4. Pour into pan & top w/ crumb mixture.

Bake 30-40 minutes or until a knife inserted in center comes out clean. Allow to cool.

Brunch Egg Braid

Because you asked for it – Marybeth Beller

Ingredients:

- 4 ounces cream cheese
- ½ cup half & half
- 8 eggs, divided
- ¼ teaspoon salt
- Dash ground black pepper
- ¼ cup red bell pepper, chopped
- 2 TB sliced green onions with tops
- 2 TB butter or margarine
- 2 pkg (8 ounces each) refrigerated crescent rolls
- ¼ pound sausage, browned
- ¼ cup (1 ounce) shredded cheddar cheese
- ¼ c. (1 ounce) shredded or diced swiss cheese

Directions:

1. Preheat oven to 375° F. Place cream cheese and milk in bowl. Microwave on HIGH 1 minute. Whisk until smooth. Separate 1 egg, reserving egg white. Add the yolk and remaining 7 eggs, salt and black pepper to bowl; whisk lightly to combine, leaving most yolks intact.
2. Heat non-stick pan over medium heat. Add butter to egg mixture, then pour into pan. Cook. approximately 60 – 90 seconds, remove from heat for 20 seconds & stir w/ spatula then return to heat. (don't let outside edge over cook before stirring). Repeat until eggs are set but still moist. Remove pan from heat.
3. Unroll both packages of crescent dough; do not separate. Arrange side by side, long sides together. Seal perforations and seam using fork. On longest sides cut dough into strips 1 ½ inches apart, 3 inches

deep (there will be 6 inches in the center for the filling). Arrange sausage evenly over middle of dough. Spoon eggs over ham. Sprinkle cheeses over eggs.

4. To braid, lift strips of dough across filling to meet in center, twisting each strip one turn. Continue alternating strips to form a braid. Brush lightly beaten egg white over dough. Bake 25-28 minutes or until deep golden brown. Cut into slices.

Montana Banana Bread

Because you asked for it – Jan Bonn

Ingredients:

- ¾ c. Sugar
- ¼ c. Butter
- ¼ c. Sour Cream
- 2 Eggs, lightly beaten
- 1 c. Bananas, mashed
- 2 c. Flour
- 2 tsp Baking Powder
- ½ tsp. Baking Soda
- 1 tsp Salt
- 1 tsp. Nutmeg
- 1 tsp. Cinnamon
- ¼ c. Sour Milk or Buttermilk
- 1 c. chopped nuts

Directions:

1. Preheat oven to 350°F F. Spray loaf pan with non-stick cooking spray or line with parchment paper.
2. Cream together sugar and butter.
3. Add sour cream, mix
4. Add eggs, mix
5. Add banana's, mix
6. Sift together dry ingredients & add to creamed mixture, alternately with milk.
7. Add nuts. Mix until combined.
8. Pour into pan & bake 35-45 minutes or until a knife inserted in center comes out clean. Allow to cool.
NOTE: Sour milk = 1 cup milk & 1 TB Vinegar

MEAL STARTERS
(SOUPS, SALADS & BREADS)

Hamburger-Vegetable Soup
(Thanks Betty Crocker!)

Ingredients:
- 1 ½ pounds hamburger
- 3 c. water
- 3 medium carrots, chopped
- 2 medium stalks celery, chopped
- 1 large potato, cut into ½" pieces
- 2 medium onions, chopped
- 1 can Corn
- 1 tsp Salt
- 2 tsp Seasoning Salt
- 1 tsp Bottled Brown bouquet sauce
- ½ to ½ tsp pepper
- 1 Bay leaf
- ¼ tsp dried Basil leaves
- 1 can (28 ounces) whole tomatoes

Directions:
1. Cook and stir hamburger in Dutch oven until light brown; drain.
2. Stir in remaining ingredients; break up tomatoes with fork. Heat to boiling
3. Reduce heat. Cover & simmer just until vegetables are tender – about 20 minutes.
4. Top w/ shredded cheese to serve.

Tomato Bisque Soup
(Nine Quarter Circle Ranch cookbook)
Because you asked for it – Cindy Haugen

Ingredients

- ¼ c. each, diced celery & onion
- 1 TB Butter
- 1 TB Flour
- ¾ c. Milk
- ¾ c. Chicken Broth
- Pinch each of Salt & Pepper
- 1 c. Diced Tomatoes (canned)
- 1 TB Honey
- ¼ tsp. Crushed fresh Basil (may use dry if no fresh available)

Directions:

1. Melt butter in medium sauce pan. Add carrots & onion & sauté until tender.
2. Stir in flour & cook for 1 minute.
3. Stir in milk, bring to simmer until slightly thickened. Keep warm until tomatoes are ready.
4. In separate pot, heat tomatoes, honey & basil for 10 minutes.
5. Place tomatoes in food processor & process till smooth.
6. Carefully & slowly add tomatoes into milk mixture. Stir. Serve hot.

Mandarin Orange & Red Onion Salad
(Nine Quarter Circle Ranch cookbook)

Dressing:
- 2 Tbsp Lemon Juice
- 2 tsp Dijon Mustard
- ½ tsp Sugar
- ½ tsp Salt
- ¼ tsp Pepper
- ½ cup Salad Oil

Combine first five ingredients. Then whisk in oil

Salad:
1 c. Sliced Almonds
1 T. Butter
1 Head Romaine, torn

1 can (11oz) Mandarin
Oranges, drained
1 Red Onion, thin sliced

1. Sauté almonds in butter until golden, drain on paper towels and put aside for garnish.
2. Combine romaine, oranges and onion (reserve a little of each). Toss with dressing.
3. Top w/ reserved oranges & onion, then top with Almonds & Serve.

Winter Salad

Because you asked for it – Marcia Rymarchyk

Ingredients:

- 4 c. chopped Iceberg lettuce
- 1 green apple, diced small
- ½ c. Sugared Walnuts
- ½ c. Craisins
- ¼ c. Bleu Cheese Crumbles
- Mustard Vinaigrette (see Below)

Lightly dress lettuce with vinaigrette. Add other ingredients. Toss slightly. Serve

Mustard Vinaigrette

½ c. Vegetable Oil
¼ c. Cider Vinegar
¼ c. Maple Syrup
1 TB Dijon

2 tsp Stone Ground Mustard
½ tsp. Garlic Salt
½ tsp. Pepper

Place all ingredients in blender or food processor. Process till smooth. Store in refrigerator.

Chicken Salad (for Sandwiches, Salads or Wraps)

Because you asked for it – Morianna Steele

Ingredients:
- 1 Chicken Breast
- 1 TB olive oil
- 2 TB each, fine diced celery & red onion
- 2 TB Dijon Mustard
- 4 TB Mayo
- Pinch Garlic Salt
- Pinch Pepper

Directions:
1. Heat oven to 350°F. Place frozen chicken breast on baking sheet. Drizzle lightly with oil and sprinkle lightly with salt & pepper. Bake 15 – 20 minutes until internal temperature reaches 165°F.
2. Cool. Chop into ½" to 1" cubes. Add celery & onion. Sprinkle lightly with garlic salt & pepper.
3. Mix Dijon & mayo together & then add to chicken. Stir. Serve on lettuce with almonds & parmesan. Or use in sandwich or wrap.

Rustic Sourdough Bread (in a dutch oven)

Because you asked for it – Judy Covington Zabenco

Ingredients:

- 2/3 c. Sourdough Starter
- 1 c. Warm Water
- 2 tsp Instant Yeast
- 1 tsp Sugar
- 2 tsp Salt
- 1 Egg
- 3 2/3 c. all-purpose flour

Directions:

1. Combine starter, water, sugar, salt, egg & yeast.
2. Stir in flour. Knead for 5 minutes.
3. Place dough in greased bowl & cover with plastic. Let rise in warm place for at least 2 hours or until tripled in size.
4. Before shaping dough, prepare another bowl that is close to the size of the rounded ball you'll be baking (approx. 8" to 9" across the top) by placing a piece of parchment in it, that will extend beyond the top of the bread in the bowl once it's put in it.
5. Gently turn out on lightly floured board & work into a dome by pulling the ball gently toward you and turning slightly to the right or left (use the bottom / pinky part of your hand to pull against the bottom of the ball). It should become a nicely rounded dome. Place the ball of dough into the prepared bowl. Cut a deep (approx. ¾") cross into the top of the ball. Cover loosely with a light towel & let rise until doubled (at least 20 or 30 minutes).
6. While the dough is rising this 2nd time, pre-heat oven to 475°F and place your 14" dutch oven in the oven to pre-heat (with the lid also).
7. Once the dough has risen, and the oven and dutch oven are hot, carefully lift the dough out of the bowl &

gently set into the dutch oven. Gently put the lid on and carefully slide it into the oven (jostling it can cause the dough to fall).

8. Bake at 450°F for 30 minutes. Remove lid & continue baking another 20 minutes or until internal temperature of 190°F.

9. Remove from dutch oven & cool on wire rack for at least 1 hour before slicing.

Swope Bread

(From Nine Quarter Circle Ranch cookbook)

Ingredients:
- 4 c. Whole Wheat Flour
- 2 c. White Flour
- 1 c. Sugar
- 2 tsp Salt
- 3 ½ c. Milk
- ½ cup Vinegar
- 2 tsp Baking Soda

Directions:
1. Heat oven to 350 degrees. Spray 2 loaf pans with non-stick spray.
2. In a large bowl (NOT a stand mixer – mix by hand!), combine flours, sugar & salt.
3. In a separate bowl, combine milk, vinegar & soda.
4. Combine the two mixtures and mix with your hands, ensuring the liquid is evenly distributed. The two mixtures will react when mixed.
5. Once thoroughly mixed, put in the prepared pans and bake for one hour or more (this is a heavy, sweet bread and so takes longer than a traditional yeast bread).

This bread is great with a hearty soup or on a cheese tray. As it "sweetens" over time, it makes a wonderful French toast.

SIDE DISHES

Broccoli Puff

Ingredients:
- 1, 10 oz. can Mushroom Soup
- 2 Eggs, Beaten
- 1 ½ c. Shredded Cheddar Cheese
- ½ c. Mayo
- 2 Tb. Onion, minced
- ½ tsp. Garlic Salt
- ¼ tsp. Pepper
- 4 Tb. Melted Butter
- 4 c. Broccoli florets

Directions:
Whisk all ingredients except broccoli. Stir in broccoli florets. Spoon into a casserole dish. Top with a little more cheese. Bake at 350 degrees for 60-90 minutes.

Herbed Red Potatoes

Ingredients:

- ~ 1 lb. Red Potatoes, cut into 1-2" chunks
- 1 c. Olive Oil
- ¼ c. Fresh Parsley, chopped
- 1 Tb. Crushed garlic
- ¼ tsp. Garlic Salt
- 1 tsp. Steak Seasoning
- 1 tsp. Dried Basil (or 1 Tb. Fresh)

Directions:
Steam potatoes till fork tender (but not too soft). Whisk remaining ingredients. Place hot potatoes in a bowl. Spoon on olive oil mixture and mix gently. Serve hot.

Herbed Corn

Ingredients:

- 6 c. Frozen Corn
- 2 c. Water
- ½ c. Butter or Margarine
- 2 Tb. Minced Fresh Parsley (or 1 Tb. Dried)
- 1 Tb. Garlic Salt
- 1 tsp. Dill Weed
- ½ tsp. Garlic Powder
- ½ tsp. Italian Seasoning
- ¼ tsp. Thyme

Directions:

Bring water and corn to boil. Reduce heat, cover & simmer till tender. Drain. Add in remaining ingredients, Stir well.

Butternut Squash

Ingredients:

- 1 Butternut Squash
- ½ c. Brown Sugar
- ¼ c. Butter
- 1 tsp. Cinnamon
- ¼ tsp. Nutmeg
- 1/8 c. Heavy Cream

Directions:

1. Cut squash in half length-wise and scoop out seeds.
2. Place face down in baking pan and add ½" – 1" water.
3. Cover tightly with foil. Bake at low temp (~250 degrees) for 2-4 hours till fork easily pierces skin and meat.
4. Remove skin from squash. Place squash chunks in stand mixer. Add butter & mix slightly. Add in rest of ingredients & mix with paddle until smooth. Spoon into casserole dish, top with a little more butter & cover tightly.
5. Return to oven at 350 degrees till hot (~1/2 hour).

Pasta w/ Sundried Tomatoes & Bacon

Ingredients:

- 2 oz. Pine Nuts
- 2/3 c. Sun-dried tomatoes in oil
- 3 Tb. Olive Oil
- 3 green onions, diced
- 4 cloves garlic, thinly sliced
- 2 Tb. Capers, rinsed
- 1 Tb. Garlic Salt
- 1 c. water
- ½ lb. Bacon, cooked & chopped
- Shredded Parmesan Cheese
- Cooked Pasta (Angel Hair but linguini, rotelli, spaghetti, all work as well)

Directions:

1. Roast pine nuts on baking sheet at 350 degrees until lightly brown (5-7 minutes). Remove & set aside.
2. Drain sun-dried tomatoes & reserve oil. Chop tomatoes into small pieces.
3. In large pan, heat olive oil and tomato oil. Sauté garlic & onions till tender.
4. Stir in water, tomatoes, capers, pine nuts, salt and bacon. Heat through.
5. Serve over pasta. Top with shredded Parmesan cheese.

ADAPTED FROM

LIFE

JOSIE

Josie stands and peers inside the cab then turns her intelligent gaze up to her Master. That gaze speaks clearly - "Must I?"

"Josie! Get IN!" he demands sternly.

She hesitates one further moment and then jumps up to the seat, quickly turning to verify she won't be left alone in this strange box. "In, Sage!" he demands to her relief as she watches her older sister obey and leap in next to her. Two pairs of intent brown eyes watch closely as the man slams the door and then moves to enter the other side.

As the box begins to rumble, Josie tucks herself close to Master as she suspiciously eyes the black hole in the dash and the bobbing stick in front of her. When the man grabs the stick & pushes it down, she cocks her head as the rumble-sound changes.

Bumping down the road in this little space, Josie carefully watches everything. Sage sits primly, eyeing the countryside, like the princess she believes herself to be would eye her subjects. Josie sees this as she hunts for wandering horses, lost cows, menacing hordes or attacking cats. She takes her job as Watcher & Guarder very seriously.

Suddenly a sound intrudes. "Bzzz...Bzzt" Oh NO! She

is the Watcher and Guarder of Runner-Kickers! She HATES Buzzer-Fliers! They don't listen to her bark and there's nowhere to nip them and they SCARE her!! Josie sinks closer to Master, tighter to his side as Sage suddenly notices the Intruder. Sage, unlike her sister, is NOT afraid of Buzzer-Fliers. But, she loves to catch them!! SNAP! SNAP! go her jaws as she tries to catch the buzzer. Josie climbs under Master's arm as she seeks to put distance between herself and the deadly battle being waged mere inches away. Sage leaps at the buzzer! Her feet are on the dash, now on the floor, and suddenly over Josie's cowering backside as the buzzer comes her way.

Desperately seeking to burrow under Master's knee, Josie is wedged into a ball. She feels no compunction to help sister - after all, doesn't she save sister from the big Runner-Kickers? Doesn't Sage flee and demand help when surrounded by those Runner-Kickers? And Josie loyally rescues sister from them! So, it's only fair that Sage save her from Buzzer-Fliers!

Suddenly, the buzz cuts off. Peeking out, Josie sees sister sitting primly once more, smacking her jaws and licking her lips. She has emerged victorious!! Josie backs out of her huddle and praises sister enthusiastically with thumping tail and kisses - just as sister does for her when Runner-Kickers have been vanquished! After all - what are sisters for?

And so, Sage and Josie return to their perusal of the passing country - one regal, one intent. Buzzer-Flier fighter complimenting Runner-Kicker fighter. Sister complimenting Sister.

Josie

Sage

MOTHERLESS CHILD

Dark night, child cold
Door opens, Mother's bold
"Enter, Midge" command comes
Slowly creeps, little one
O' Motherless Child

Cry sounds, knowledge flares
Open arms, Mother cares
"Lost parent" announced around
"Where's Momma?" desperate sound
O' Motherless Child

Busy room, machine scream
Baby whimpers, nurses clean
Father lost, mother gone
No Hope, society's pawn
O' Motherless Child

Life lived, never cherished
Siblings jealous, dreams perish
Age claims, death awaits
Mother dies… and I'm made
O' Motherless Child

SIXTY MILES OF BAD ROAD

"Sixty miles of bad road." That's what Dad always called this stretch of dusty, serpentine washboards between Hungry Horse Dam and the headwaters of the south fork of the Flathead River. While closer to 50 miles, he always figured the extra 10 were racked up while weaving back and forth across the road to avoid the largest of the potholes.

However, the hazards and history associated with getting from here to there were the last thoughts in my head that July morning. They had been eclipsed by visions of gold and silver while I contemplated my chances at fame and fortune; specifically, my chances at winning the gold buckle at the upcoming rodeo in Columbia Falls.

Having dropped Dad and the packers at the Meadowcreek trailhead on July 1st to start packing hay into camp, I was headed back up to get them a week later. Of course, it always took <u>hours</u> to get to the trailhead thanks to his "granny" driving as my brother Tim always called it. I had no intention of taking such a leisurely jaunt up the valley. And, even though I was two hours late getting started, I still figured I could make it on time.

Now mid-July in Montana is never mild. You either get rain and cold or dry and <u>hot</u>. Or both – depending on the day. So far, we'd been on the receiving end of

Sols' most powerful rays but that was rumored to be ending. However, with no sign of that reprieve in sight, I took the stock truck around the left turn of the dam and began my dusty trek south. For the first leg, I made good time. The miles were racking up in a nearly perfect ratio with the dust layers that caked on my damp skin. However, as I came around the sharp turn of Doris Creek, my time schedule took its first hit. Lying across the entire road was a load of logs. And no loader in sight. Apparently, a good ol' boy had decided to get serious about cutting and selling firewood by getting an old log truck and hauling large loads. But, he forgot to get serious about safety and the rusted cables he'd used had snapped, spilling his whole load.

When asked about time, he replied "Wal, Ah figger Ah can get the loader down 'ere in a coupla hours an' be loaded back up by supper time." As if this were a speedy recovery. Well, up here I suppose it IS, but that didn't help me none.

So, exasperated, but glad I wasn't further along, I retraced my steps north and elected to head up the east side by way of Martin city.

An hour later, I was once again ten miles into my trip. Of course, by this time, I'd already gone nearly forty! And the dust collected in the interim, mixed with the streamers of sweat, had caked into a mud worthy of any beauty regime. But, I don't think it was improving my rugged good looks quite as much as advertised.

As I waltzed Mathilda up the road, I hummed the little ditty for which she was named. Loud, a little slow, but rock solid, his Pop had said she reminded him of what waltzing with a Mathilda would entail. So, whenever one of the boys had to guide her through the serpentine curves on the reservoir road, he said he was "Waltzing Mathilda". Now, with the two o'clock sun beating down, and my schedule clock ticking away in my head, I increased my speed to try and make up time, while simultaneously digging into the cooler for some refreshment.

It was, of course, about now that some yahoo in his Expedition came screaming around the corner at Dudley creek. Now driving a loaded stock truck, for those of you haven't seen one, is a bit like steering an elephant on roller skates. While mine was empty that day, it was still akin to riding a crate on wheels. Jerking the wheel a fraction too late on a contraption a mite too slow, resulted in the racing Expedition driver being around the turn and out of sight as Mathilda's tires grabbed the soft shoulder and slowly pulled the truck to the right. As the roll started, it felt a bit like a funhouse tunnel in slow motion. Culminating in a soft but decisive landing on her side, the wreck was the ultimate symbol of my smashed plan.

As I trudged along the inner edge of the curve at Hungry Horse creek after dragging myself out of the overturned cab, I was distracting myself from the heat and dust with daydreams of caramel milkshakes and air conditioning while sharing a burger with my girl at the A&W in Columbia Falls. So immersed was I in my fantasy, that that the first warning huff didn't penetrate. The second one shot clear to my core. Frozen in mid-stride, all thoughts focused on what I'd heard. The only movement was my eyes, darting back and forth trying to identify the location of the sound – and the slow tilt of my body sideways as my raised foot started to drag. Quickly losing my balance and my nerve, I completed my step with a pivot on the lowered limb to glance cautiously behind. Sure enough, there stood an angry sow grizzly. As if to reinforce this tardy realization, she gave a third huff-growl and emphasized her ire with a hop forward.

Columbia Falls high school, while small and "rural", never-the-less was a first-rate "educatory facility" – or so Grandma always believed and told anyone who'd listen – and even some who didn't. I wasn't entirely on board with her assessment, but I did have to admit that the administration did a first-rate job on safety instruction. They had, in fact, had a ranger come in to teach "bear safety" during spring quarter. This was how I knew that in order for this mama to be so put-out, I had to be between her and something she valued, like a cub or her favorite berry patch. Seeing no berries in sight, I quickly deduced a cub must be in close proximity.

During that same lecture on *"Ursus horribilis"*, I remembered hearing that running and screaming are poor options and my best chance for survival was to slowly back away from the sow and her cub and offer no threatening eye contact or movement. But, my best friend Charles, always maintained that you should run downhill from a bear as they are incapable of running as fast down as they can up. So, after weighing expertise against myth, and calling on every internal resource I possessed, I turned and ran as fast as rubberized legs would carry me, downhill towards the reservoir.

If my arms had been encased in blowsy linen rather than cotton short-sleeves, my windmilling would have pumped gallons of water as my out-of-control legs dodged boulders and craters, bowling me through alder and willow brush. My arrival at the tenuous safety of the reservoir was sudden and dramatic. One moment I was batting at branches as they slapped my arms and face, the next I was pedaling over open water, into which I dropped like the proverbial stone. My flailing led to sputtering but quickly switched to a unique half crawl, half dog paddle technique which finally propelled me a short distance from shore.

Treading water and gasping as quietly as possible, I strained to hear if the angry sow had pursued me. While no grunts, roars or crashing brush heralded an immediate arrival, the vision of a grizzly crouching just out of sight and awaiting my shore landing, wouldn't leave my mind. So, with the same lurch and kick technique, I began propelling myself south along the shoreline.

Even a young man's stamina has limits and eventually I was forced to find an opening in the brush and pull myself on shore. As I laid there gasping, I tried to find a silver-lining by noticing that at least the caked mud had washed off. As I waited for the sun to dry me, however, I gradually realized there was no sun. Just as that understanding settled like a wet blanket over my tired consciousness, I opened my eyes to see the silver-lined cloud burst wide open, releasing torrents of cold water.

Jumping to my size 10 feet, I pushed and fought my way into the shelter of a giant fir tree where I prepared to wait out the summer thunder-boomer. Just as I got settled, however, the rain quit as quickly as it had started and the sun once again revealed its golden face. Muttering under my breath about the vagaries of weather, people, animals, and life in general, I started the short but steep climb back up to the road.

Sometime later, I had attained the road and resumed my trek along its no longer dusty track. The sun had warmed and dried my clothes and I was beginning to feel my spirits lift once again. Elevating my mood even higher, a battered pickup truck pulled alongside and asked if they could give me "a lift for distance?" Within moments I was comfortably ensconced in the truck bed, atop a pile of dusty and well-worn camping equipment. The bearded driver had apologized over the arrangement but there just wasn't room in the cab, as it was filled to bursting with a wife, two kids, and their dog. Just happy to not be moving under my own power, I settled in and enjoyed the view.

By the time I was dropped off at the junction of the east and west roads at the south end of the reservoir, I was even optimistic about my arrival at the trailhead. The family had expressed their regrets at being unable to take me all the way to Bunker Creek trailhead, but it was another hour in the wrong direction, and they still had several hours before they would arrive at their ultimate destination of Beaver Creek at the furthest point on the road. So, with enthusiastic waves and the offer of a cold Coke, they left me as I turned and begin the next leg of my far too eventful journey.

After holding the icy can against my neck for a moment, I popped the top in preparation for the refreshing treat. The resultant refreshment was not how I had imagined. The impressive fountain of sugar-laden liquid cascaded over hair and neck, running in rivulets down the inside of my shirt and leaving my head, shoulders, arm and hand coated in a sticky and restrictive glaze. Unable to spawn even the smallest degree of surprise at this latest calamity,

I just tipped the can to my lips and drained the final two inches of soda. Then I once again started walking.

It only took a mile for the bees to find me, although once they arrived, I was surprised they hadn't shown up sooner. After all, I did reek of nectar. I was like a giant lottery win for them. With no way to cover up to keep them from landing on me, I resorted to cutting several willow branches and using both hands to brandish them about my head. From a distance, I must have appeared as if I was batting at the voices in my head. Which, apparently, is what the few vehicles that passed me thought, as they rolled up windows and hurried past.

Nearly ninety minutes and six miles had passed, when a young bohemian on an ailing motorcycle finally stopped alongside and asked if I needed help. Even assuming that he had his OWN voices and so wasn't intimidated by my apparent, if invisible, entourage, I wasn't about to turn down his offer. So, after I finished explaining that I needed to get to the end of the road – another 4 miles – he readily agreed to give me a lift. Of course, that meant me sharing the bike and once I was aboard, I realized that his personal aura was even more piercing than my own. Except, in his case, horseflies were the horde that followed. And so, presumably trailing a swarm of flying armies, we proceeded to the corrals where I found my dad and his crew waiting.

After watching me crawl off the ancient motorcycle and thank the long-haired Good Samaritan, my dad looked me up and down and asked "What the hell happened to you boy? You look like sixty miles of bad road!"

MAIN DISHES & CASSEROLES

Hereford Casserole
(or as our son called it: "Heifer Casserole")

Ingredients:
- 1 ½ lb Hamburger
- ½ yellow onion, diced
- 2 TB garlic, minced
- 4.5 cups uncooked pasta (macaroni, rotini, fusilli, etc.)
- 1 jar (14oz) Spaghetti sauce
- 4 oz. Cream Cheese, softened
- 1 c. Sour Cream
- 1 can (8oz) Cream of Mushroom Soup
- 1 c. Cheddar Cheese, shredded

Directions:
1. Brown hamburger, diced onions & garlic. Drain off excess fat.
2. Meanwhile, cook pasta according to package directions, drain.
3. Add Spaghetti sauce to meat mixture.
4. In a small bowl, beat cream cheese until smooth.
5. Add sour cream and soup, beat until blended.
6. Add pasta to soup mixture.
7. Spoon half of beef mixture into a casserole dish (13x9)
8. Top with pasta/soup mixture & remaining beef mixture. Sprinkle w/ cheese.
9. Bake uncovered, at 350°F for 35-45 minutes or until heated through & cheese is melted.

Spring Fling Casserole

Ingredients

- 2 Russet or 4 Red potatoes, cut into 1" chunks (peel russets)
- 2-4 carrots, diced
- 1 c. diced onion
- 1 Polska Kielbasa into 1" pieces
- 2 c. corn (I prefer frozen, but can use fresh or canned)
- 1 c. frozen peas
- 1 c. frozen green beans (or canned)
- 2 TB Seasoning Salt
- 2 TB Lemon Juice
- 2 TB Butter
- 1 c. Shredded Cheddar Cheese

Directions:

1. In large baking dish, layer ingredients in order given.
2. Sprinkle with seasoning salt, then lemon juice.
3. Top with dots of butter.
4. Cover tightly and bake at 350°F for 1 to 1 ½ hours until potatoes and carrots are fork tender.
5. Stir well and top with cheese.
6. Return to oven, uncovered, 10-15 minutes or until cheese is melted.
7. Serve.

Notes:

- If I have time, I prefer to sauté the carrots & onions first, with a little garlic.
- You can substitute a bag of frozen mixed veggies for any of the fresh/frozen ones. I usually add extra corn if I do this.
- It's also great with fresh cabbage, cut into strips & added on top of the beans.

Pulled Pork

Because you asked for it – Jeromy Allen

Ingredients:
- 2-3# Pork Roast (or leftover pork of any sort)
- 1, 16oz bottle Dr. Pepper or Coke
- 2 TB Montreal Steak Seasoning
- 1 to 2 cups BBQ Sauce (whatever you like)

Directions:
1. If using leftover pork, jump to #6
2. Pre-heat oven to 275°F - 300°F
3. Spray heavy pot (cast iron dutch oven works great) with non-stick spray. Place pork roast in pot & sprinkle with steak seasoning. Pour soda around roast & cover tightly with lid or double thickness of aluminum foil.
4. Place in oven & bake 4-6 hours or until it pulls apart easily. (Check after 2-3 hours to ensure it still has plenty of liquid).
5. Remove from oven & pull apart. (At this point you can stick in fridge until you're ready to go to next step).
6. Ensure pork is warm to touch (may need to return to oven or microwave to bring to approx. 125°F). Pour BBQ sauce over top & use tongs to turn & mix it through the meat. Cover tightly & return to oven until heated through (20 – 40 minutes). Serve hot on buns with cheese, over potatoes or however you like, and with extra sauce on side.

Baked Pork Chops

Because you asked for it – Alicia Hilmo

Ingredients:

- ¼ c. Kosher Salt
- 1 c. Flour (can substitute almond or coconut flour for Keto or gluten-free)
- 4-6 Thick cut Pork Chops
- 1 TB Seasoning Salt (I use Lawry's)
- Crisco for frying

Directions:

1. Dissolve salt in water in large bowl. Add pork chops. Let brine for at least 12 hours or overnight.
2. Dry chops on paper towels & then dredge in flour / seasoning salt mixture. Heat oven to 300°F.
3. Heat thin layer of Crisco in heavy skillet until fairly hot. Add pork chops & fry until browned. Flip & brown other side.
4. Remove to baking pan with an elevated grate in the bottom of it to keep chops up off the bottom.
5. Add water just to bottom of grate. Cover pan tightly with 2 layers of aluminum foil.
6. Bake in oven 2 ½ to 3 hours, or until very tender. Serve with applesauce.

DESSERTS

Zucchini – Chocolate Cookies
Because you asked for it – Lorri Dixon

Ingredients:
- 2/3 c. Chocolate Chips, melted & Cooled
- 2 c. Flour
- ¼ c. Cocoa
- 1 tsp Baking Soda
- ½ tsp Salt
- ½ c. butter, softened
- ¼ c. Sugar
- ½ c. Brown Sugar
- 1 Egg
- 1 tsp Vanilla
- 1 c. Zucchini, shredded
- 1 c. Chocolate Chips

Directions:
1. Preheat oven to 325°F
2. Whisk flour, cocoa, soda & salt together
3. Cream together butter & sugars
4. Add egg & vanilla & cream again
5. Stir in Zucchini.
6. Stir in melted chocolate
7. Stir in dry ingredients
8. Stir in chocolate chips
9. Roll into 1.5" to 2" balls, place 2" apart on baking sheet. Bake 10-11 minutes

Strawberry Rhubarb Pie

Ingredients:

Crust:
- 2 c. All-purpose Flour
- ½ c. Cake flour
- 3 tsp. sifted Powdered Sugar
- ½ c. Crisco (butter flavored)
- ½ c. Salted Butter
- Pinch Salt
- 1 Egg
- 2 tsp. Vinegar
- ¼ c. Water

Filling:
- 2 ½ c. chopped rhubarb
- 2 ½ c. Strawberries (washed, stemmed & cut)
- 1 ½ c. Sugar
- 2 TB Minute Tapioca
- 1 TB Flour
- ½ tsp. Lemon Zest
- ½ tsp. Lemon Juice
- ½ tsp. Ground Cinnamon
- 1 tsp. Vanilla Extract
- 3 TB. Butter, cubed small
- 1 Egg White, beaten w/ 1 tsp water

Directions:

Crust:
1. Mix flours, salt and powdered sugar together.
2. Cut in butter and Crisco until mixture is crumbly.
3. Whisk egg, vinegar & water together & then gently mix into dry mixture until just combined.
4. Chill 15 minutes, wrapped tightly.
5. Roll out into desired pie pan size & lay into pie pan.
6. Roll out tops & carefully set aside.

Filling:
1. Mix fruit, sugar, tapioca, flour, zest and juice, cinnamon, and vanilla.
2. Pour into prepared crust.
3. Top with butter. Brush edges of pie crust with egg white wash.
4. Place top crust over filling. Crimp edges.
5. Brush with egg white wash.

6. Collar with foil or pie ring and bake at 425°F for 15 minutes. Decrease temperature to 375°F and bake another 45-50 minutes or until filling is bubbly.
7. Let cool before serving.

Cowboy Cookies

Ingredients:
- 2 ½ c. Margarine
- 1 ½ c. Brown Sugar
- 1 ½ c. Sugar
- 2 Eggs
- 2 tsp. Vanilla Extract
- 3 c. Flour
- 2 tsp. Baking Soda
- 2 tsp. Salt
- 2 T. Cinnamon
- 1 tsp. Nutmeg
- 4 c. Oats
- 2 c. Coconut
- 2 c. Chocolate Chips
- 2 c. Raisins
- 1 ½ c. Chopped Nuts

Directions:
1. Mix margarine, sugar, eggs and vanilla.
2. Combine with rest of ingredients.
3. Drop on greased cookie sheet.
4. Bake at 350°F for 10-15 minutes

Old-Fashioned Bread Pudding w/ Caramel Rum Sauce

Because you asked for it - Kathleen Hennagin

Ingredients:

Bread Pudding:
- Cubed bread to fill dish (approx. 8 cups)
- 4 eggs
- 1 c. Half & Half
- 2 c. Heavy Cream
- 1 ½ c. Whole Milk
- 1 c. Sugar
- 1 TB Vanilla
- 2 tsp Cinnamon

Caramel Rum Sauce:
- ¼ c. butter
- ¼ c. brown sugar
- ¼ c. white sugar
- ½ c. Heavy Cream
- 3 TB Rum

Directions:

1. Pre-heat oven to 350°F, Spray 9x13 dish with non-stick cooking spray. Spread bread in dish (you want it to the top of the dish, but you don't need to press it in)
2. Pour the half and half over the bread & allow it to soak in while you mix everything else together.
3. Whisk together eggs, heavy cream, milk, sugar, vanilla & cinnamon. Pour over the bread. (You want it to fill the dish almost to the top. If it doesn't, just pour some more whole milk around the top to fill it up.)
4. Bake 45 minutes – 1 hour, or until the center is set and just moist (don't let it get too dry) and the bread on top is golden. Let cool slightly before serving. Top with sauce & whipped cream.

CARAMEL RUM SAUCE:

1. Melt butter in small saucepan.
2. Add sugars & cook while stirring for approx. 2 minutes until caramel sauce has formed.
3. Remove from heat & add rum (carefully so it doesn't flare up). Return to heat & cook, stirring constantly, for another 2-3 minutes.
4. Remove from heat & stir in heavy cream. Return to heat & simmer for 8 – 10 minutes. Serve hot.

Pecan Tassies

Ingredients:

Pastry Cups:
- 1 c. flour
- ¼ c. cornmeal
- ½ c. butter or margarine
- 1 package cream cheese, softened

Pecan Filling
- ½ c. brown sugar
- ¼ c. molasses
- 3 tbsp. bourbon
- 1 tbsp. butter
- 1/8 tsp of salt
- 2/3 c. pecans, chopped
- 1 large egg

Directions

1. **Prepare Pastry Cups:** Preheat oven to 350 degrees F. Combine flour and cornmeal in small bowl. In mixer bowl, at medium speed, beat butter and cream cheese until creamy. Reduce speed to low; gradually beat in flour mixture until crumbly. Turn out mixture onto floured board and lightly knead dough until it holds together, shape into a ball.
2. Divide dough into 24 equal pieces. With fingertips, gently press each piece of dough evenly onto bottom and up sides of twelve muffin-pan cups. (If nonstick pan is not available, grease cups.)
3. **Prepare Pecan Filling:** In medium bowl, with wire whisk or fork, mix sugar, molasses, bourbon, butter, salt, and egg until blended. Stir in pecans. Spoon about 1 tablespoon filling into each pastry cup. Top with 1 whole Pecan.
4. Bake 25 - 35 minutes or until filling is set and edges of crusts are golden. With tip of knife, gently loosen tassies from pans and transfer to wire rack to cool completely. Store tassies, with waxed paper between layers, in tightly covered container at room temperature up to 1 week, or in freezer up to 3 months.

Beet Cake

Ingredients:
- 4 eggs
- 2 c. sugar
- 1 c. vegetable oil
- 2 c. flour
- 2 tsp baking powder
- 1 ½ tsp. baking soda
- 1 tsp. cinnamon
- 2 tsp. vanilla
- 3 c. shredded fresh beets
- 1 c. chopped walnuts

Directions:
1. Heat oven to 350 °F, grease and flour 13x9 baking pan.
2. Beat eggs, sugar and oil until light and fluffy.
3. Sift together flour, baking powder, baking soda and cinnamon.
4. Add to egg mixture and mix well.
5. Add vanilla, beets and walnuts.
6. Beat for 1 minute on medium speed.
7. Pour into pan, bake for 45 minutes, or until a pick comes out clean.

Peach Cobbler

Ingredients:
- 1 Tb Butter
- 6 Lg Peaches
- 1 1/3 c. Bisquick
- 1 Tb Sugar
- ½ c. Sugar
- 1 c. Milk
- Milk, Ice Cream or Whip Cream
- 1 Tb. Oil
- 1 tsp ground nutmeg
- 1 tsp Ground Cinnamon
- 1 Tb Cornstarch
- ½ c. Boiling Water

Directions:
1. Melt butter and pour into bottom of a 9-inch square pan or 10-inch Dutch oven.
2. Lay peaches in even layer on bottom.
3. Mix together baking mix, 1 Tb Sugar, milk, and oil. Spread evenly over peaches
4. Mix together remaining ½ c. Sugar, cinnamon, nutmeg & cornstarch. Sprinkle evenly over dough.
5. Pour boiling water over top, making sure all sugar mixture is moistened.
6. Bake at 350 degrees for 35-45 minutes.
7. FOR DUTCH OVENS: Place 3-4 coals underneath, and 10-12 on top. Allow to bake for at least 1.5 – 2 hours.
8. Serve warm with desired topping.

(Note – canned peaches may be used)

SAUCES, MARINADES & MISC

Sweet / Spicy Marinade for Flank Steak

Ingredients:
- 2 Tb. Montreal Steak Seasoning
- 2 Tb. Chopped Garlic
- 1 qt. Coca-Cola

Directions:
Combine all ingredients. Allow steak to marinate for at least 12 hours.

Chimichurri Sauce (for red meats)

Ingredients:
- 4 Garlic Cloves
- 1 c. Fresh Parsley
- 1/3 c. Olive Oil
- ¼ c. Fresh Tarragon
- 1 Tb. Champagne Vinegar
- ¼ tsp. Red Pepper Flakes
- ¼ tsp. Pepper
- ¼ tsp. Garlic Salt
- 1 Tb. Lemon Juice
- ¼ c. Fresh Oregano
- ¼ c. Fresh Chives

Directions:
Place all ingredients in food processor. Pulse until desired consistency.

Jezebel Sauce (for pork and white meats)

Ingredients:
- 20 oz. Crushed Pineapple
- 15 oz. Apple Jelly
- 5 oz. Horseradish
- 2 oz. Dry Mustard
- 1 tsp. Black Pepper

Directions:
Mix together & keep refrigerated. Lasts indefinitely.

FANTASY

LIFE

ANNABELLE

Annabelle squatted in the corner. Faded and old, her mahogany raiment lost its glamour to the heavy layer of dust coating her arms, feet, and keys. Dozing the time away, she seldom surfaced to the present. But, that afternoon, a child plunking a handful of keys abruptly awakened her.

"Marcy! Don't touch that. It bothers people!" Annabelle heard the reproach with a sagging spirit. It had been ages since a youngster had labored over her ivories. A child's determination and astonishment at the music they could draw forth brought joy to Annabelle's quiet life. The first youngster to own Annabelle had been the "Original Annabelle." The young girl's father had traveled all the way to New York to purchase a piano for his six-year-old's birthday. Annabelle recalled her first encounter with what would be her founding family.

"This is a beautiful piece of work. My daughter will love it. Please prepare it to be shipped to Hawthorne, Nevada. Do you have a pen I could borrow? Thank-you." He had proceeded to lift the Steinway's lid and inside he printed "To Annabelle on her sixth birthday. Love, Dad." The name Annabelle had stuck with the piano through her long and varied life.

That little six-year-old fell in love at first sight with the instrument and its deep patina. She immediately sat on the stool and twirled till she was giddy. Then she sobered and sat staring at the keys. "Oh, Daddy! She's wonderful. I'll learn to play her splendidly!" The girl had been as good as her vow. For sixteen years they'd known each other. Eventually, however, the young lady had married and moved to California with her new husband. When her parents aged, they followed, in order to be close to their only child.

Other children had followed little Annabelle, each with his or her own ambitions. Lucy had been one of six children belonging to the next owners. All six had learned to play on Annabelle, but Lucy was the only one who truly loved her. She grew first into a teenage flapper. She'd stay out late with friends and then bring them home in the wee hours to dance some more to the ragtime she'd belt out on Annabelle. When she next grew into a stunning young woman, their good times had come to an abrupt end.

"I'll miss you, Annabelle. We've had such wonderful times together. But, it's time for me to get married and have children of my own. My new house is too little for you, and so I can't take you with me. I'm so very sorry." Annabelle was left behind, forgotten eventually by Lucy and ignored by the elders. She stayed in that corner, alone, until the house was sold.

"Oh my! Look at this old piano. She'll be beautiful when all polished up. What a wonderful bonus!" They hugged each other, glowing with their good fortune. Finding her name, they too promptly called her Annabelle. Their son, Gerald, learned to play superbly. His parents kept Annabelle in perfect shape. When he went off to WWII, Annabelle felt the loss as keenly as his parents. When he came home on leave, a joyous occasion ensued, with music and dancing and laughter. Then - one time - he left and never returned.

Annabelle remembered his mother's tears. "Oh Annabelle, I'll miss the beautiful music you two created," she'd said as she slowly polished Annabelle's face. Tears rolled down her cheeks as she came to grief with her child's death. Occasionally through the years, she'd sit on Annabelle's stool and reminisce about Gerald as she rubbed oil into Annabelle's aged countenance and polished their shared memories. She had been the only non-player Annabelle had ever noticed. Their shared loneliness was an unknown but steadfast bond. When the house was once again sold, a childless couple turned it into a roadside inn, which they called "Annabelle's" after finding the dedication secreted under her lid cap. While they didn't play, they kept Annabelle in shape for any guests who might wish to tickle her strings. Those first ten years with the young couple brought many new experiences for Annabelle.

A new schoolteacher in Hawthorne, Ms. Campbell, had stayed at the Inn for six months before she found her own apartment. Every night she'd play for forty-five cultured minutes to the enjoyment of Annabelle and the guests.

"Annabelle, you make Bach and Mozart lovelier than I've ever played them on other piano's. It's a delight to play the refined composers with you." Annabelle found her soft touch and classical interpretation refreshing.

Another time, a teenager from California had rented a room for one night. Annabelle heard the young proprietors whispering that she looked like a runaway. That evening the young girl had sat at the keys and played hauntingly sad songs. Upon hearing Annabelle's name, she became disconsolate and simply laid her head on crossed arms over Annabelle and softly cried. While Annabelle never heard or understood the girl's plight, she felt oddly attached to her. The next morning, the girl trailed a hand across Annabelle's cover as she reluctantly left. Annabelle heard the "screech – whoosh" of the bus as it enfolded the troubled one. Annabelle regretted never hearing the teenager's name or knowing how she fared.

Once a truly amazing night had occurred. During a vicious thunderstorm, two young men had been blown in by the wind and rain. "The damn convertible broke down. We're on our way home from a show but need someplace to flop 'til the ride we called gets here, " was the explanation Annabelle overheard. She didn't listen too closely, dismissing them as non-players. Then one of the men spotted her. "All right! Now we can <u>really</u> pass the time!"

"Go to it Jerry!" the other encouraged. Jerked from her mistiness by a forceful slide down her keys, Annabelle abruptly reassessed the men. Jerry began playing her like no one since Lucy. As he pounded away, he was singing a song Annabelle had, unbelievably, never heard. However, she knew that "Great Balls of Fire" would move her as nothing else from that day on. By the time the storm abated and Jerry and his friend left, Annabelle was vibrating, bruised, tired, and yet strangely exhilarated. Rock and Roll had changed her forever.

Unfortunately, her only recent companions were the servicemen from the nearby air force base. A few officers rented rooms at the inn and occasionally a family member would visit. Annabelle still heard the people come and go on the bus, but few lingered over her faded glory. Never for more than a few quick plunks on the keys, and those usually by children like Marcy. The same couple still managed the inn, but the drop off in guests had forced cutbacks. Annabelle's tuner was the first casualty.

As Marcy's mother dragged her protesting offspring to the door, another shadow crept up Annabelle's stool. A leathered hand ran lightly down her keys and then braced the fragile body that eased onto the stool. The touch felt oddly familiar, but Annabelle couldn't reconcile the features behind it.

"Grandma? Are you ok? You're tired. Why didn't we stop at the motel ten miles back instead of pushing on here?" A voice intruded on Annabelle's ruminations.

"Mark, lift the lid and see if anything is written there," said the ancient voice while ignoring his questions.

Mark closed his eyes momentarily and gritted his teeth. Sighing, he pushed up on the lid. The hinges creaked as he struggled to make them swing. "There's something, but it's faded. Let's see, I think it says 'To Annabelle on her sixth birthday. Love, Dad' Why's your name here Grandma?"

"I'm the Annabelle this lovely instrument was given to. I never thought she'd still be here in my old home."

The rest of the evening, the Annabelles played together. They ran the gamut from learning rhymes "Every good boy does fine" to the classics of Chopin and even a little ragtime and rock. Late that night, the frail woman reluctantly retired to a room down the hall. Her newly patient grandson had quietly absorbed the sounds of nostalgia emanating from the tired keys and fingers.

The next day, Original Annabelle said a final goodbye and allowed herself to be led to the waiting car. Shortly after her departure, the no-longer-so-young proprietors came to stand by Annabelle.

"It's silly to talk to a piano," the man said.

"She's touched so many lives, it only seems fitting to at least explain," his wife's gray eyes implored him.

He sighed resignedly and began. "Annabelle, you know we've had money problems lately, and well, we got a good offer." He looked expectantly at his wife.

"The man says you'll have a good home. He promised," she said, her eyes large with unexpected sadness. "I'm sorry."

They turned and escaped the resentment they imagined emanating from the dusty wood. Loaded into a moving van two hours later, Annabelle felt the straps tighten and watched her only home sink from view as the ramp raised and the bolt shot closed.

BELLE'S OF FREEDOM

The bells of Freedom, Montana were calling the Lutheran faithful to worship when Chloe awoke in her own little Hell, her swollen cheek pressed against the pumpkin shag carpet. From her prone position, she could see the shards of the broken floor lamp she'd just found last week at the thrift store, scattered across the room. At least it wasn't on and shining in her eyes. She didn't think she could stand the pain a bright room would have sent lancing through her head.

As she gathered herself and pushed to her feet, she determinedly kept her mind from dwelling on the previous night – or even the preceding years. Pulling a green hoodie over her dirty white tank top, Chloe stepped into her unlaced sneakers while hitching up her baggy "Juicy" sweats. No socks, but she barely noticed as she rolled her taut shoulders and dug a Virginia Slim out of her purse. Lighting up, she grabbed her last $20 and slipped out the door into the bright morning light. Wincing as she slunk down the sidewalk towards the little corner grocery that served Freedom's 212 residents, she heard the Methodists begin pealing their own bells and knew the Baptists would follow suit in another 30 minutes at 11am, on the dot. A person could literally tell time by the bells in Freedom, like a village from the Middle Ages where one's life was twined irrevocably with the town church. Most days, the bells rang at 8am, noon, and

7:30pm, and on Sundays, those times were bolstered by the tolling of the morning calls to service. Chloe had never lived anywhere that had such audible reminders of the time and she idly wondered why Freedom was so proud of its bells that it felt the need to ring them so frequently.

As she crossed the street towards the mercantile, she saw Toodles tottering towards her. As they neared each other in the center of the street, she could feel the old woman eyeing her face and saw the frown that pulled all the old woman's creases south like winter calling to the birds.

Chloe wasn't in the mood for questions, so she hastily averted her eyes and tried to scoot past the crone as quickly as possible, edging to the outside of the crosswalk marks. As she passed, however, Chloe was shocked to feel her hand caught in one of Toodles'. The old, wise brown eyes softened as she took Chloe's hands between both her own. Chloe could feel the papery-dry, but feathery soft skin pressing her palms and she flashed back to her too-brief childhood.

Nana had been her father's grandmother and was old before Chloe was even born. When her father, Dave, died just after Chloe's birth, Nana had tried to help his young wife and child. But, boyfriend number whatever had forbidden either of them to visit Nana – her eyes were too sharp he said. Besides, they didn't need reminding of "Saint David" either. Because that boyfriend stuck around awhile, Chloe had seldom seen

Nana. By the time he left, and Mom had married boyfriend number whatever plus two, Chloe was afraid Nana would see the guilt in her with those sharp eyes. The only clear memory of Nana she still retained was the feel of those gentle, silky hands stroking her cheek while tendrils of lilac scent twirled around their heads.

Chloe shook her head to clear the memory and tried to free her hand from Toodles' soft grip. But, the ancient tightened her hold and looked Chloe in the eye with a knowing but gentle gaze.

"When Freedom's bells ring for the new day, it will be the time to choose to ring your own bell of freedom or you may never lose your bonds."

With those cryptic words, she pressed Chloe's hand one more time and then released her, turning to continue her way to the 1st Methodist Church of Freedom. Chloe stood staring after Toodles until old man Scriver honked his horn and she realized she still stood in the center of the crosswalk with her hand held out in front of her like a penitent reaching for her Savior. She snatched back the traitorous limb and scuttled on across the road.

Once inside the mercantile's front entrance, Chloe paused for a moment to consider her options. The $20 would need to last until Jay turned back up with more cash, and that could be hours or days. Or weeks. Two minutes of intense calculations and then she quickly settled on a pack of cigarettes, a loaf of bread, a jar of peanut butter, a jug of Kool-Aid mix, and six Kit Kats.

As she stepped to the small, chipped linoleum counter and dug out the twenty, Jill Kimball breezed through the heavy front door, setting off a chorus of chimes from the sleigh bells hung to alert employees when a new customer walked in. Chloe's attempt to hide behind the card display rack was loudly proven unsuccessful when Jill squealed like she'd found a diamond ring and rushed over to grab Chloe's arm in an enthusiastic display of friendship.

"Chloe! Where've you been! I tried calling all week and stopped by the house like a dozen times and I could never ..." Suddenly her voice trailed off as her eyes lit on Chloe's face. "What was it this time?" she asked flatly. "The phone ring too loud? Tuesday arrive too soon? Were you breathing too much?"

Chloe knew of Jill's dislike for Jay, but it hurt her to have the two of them at odds. "Really, Jill, it's nothing. It was an accident."

Jill snorted and opened her mouth for a retort, but Chloe quickly continued to forestall an unpleasant discussion. "Hey Jilly, I had the strangest run-in with Toodles this morning. She said something about 'When the bells of Freedom ring the new day'. Do you have any idea what that means?"

"Oh my GOSH!" Jilly squealed. "You've never heard that story?"

Chloe shook her head and asked "What story?"

Jilly grabbed Chloe's arm again as she was picking up her change from the young cashier and pulled her to the small aisle near the counter, where dusty fishing lures and other potential last-minute sporting items were on display. Judging by the faded lettering and dust on most of the items, few fishermen or bird hunters wandered in – or those that did were already well-prepared. Leaning on the wooden rack with "Assorted Sale Items", Jilly settled in to regale Chloe with some of Freedom's history. Chloe, still battling a headache and trying to avoid reminding Jilly of her bruise, turned sideways to Jilly and put her back to the painful sunshine streaming through the windows.

"Okay, so here's what Granny told me, although PawPaw always says the story's been embellished by the "wimmen". Of course, I figure that the man just don't like the idea of any female 'rescuing' them! I mean, you know how Artie gets when... Oh, right, Sorry!" She laughed as she caught Chloe's "get on with it" look. With that, she finally settled into story mode.

"Back when Freedom was newly founded in the mid-1870s, there were still 'hostiles' wandering this part of the country. To help give the settlers in the new town a chance to prepare for any sudden raids, the ladies of the town suggested a dawn to dusk "watch" be set up in the church tower. Knowing most tribes preferred to attack in the daylight, they figured this would help the town be alerted in case a raiding party took a notion to attack. A rotation schedule was set up with everyone over the age of ten taking a two-hour stint. This meant each person really only had one shift per week or less. When anyone saw the slightest suspicious thing out on the prairie, they'd ring the church bell and everyone within hearing would rush to bar doors, grab rifles and get in place. It only took once or twice for the few hostile groups left to come to the understanding that 'Freedom ain't easy'.

"It was only a couple years before Freedom grew enough and the tribes were subdued enough that the 'Belles of Freedom' as the ladies program was called, was no longer necessary. So, while the watch was disbanded, the tradition was kept. If any emergency threatened, Freedom's bells would ring. With the exception of a few fires, the bells were seldom rung outside of Sunday services. But, as we grew and more churches were established, the tradition continued.

Then, in 1920, a new crisis settled in Freedom overnight. While the war was "over" it would still be some months or even years before all the men came home. So, it was left to the women and children and old men to take care of the town. Well, a local bootlegger decided to capitalize on the newly passed Prohibition by smuggling stuff across the border from Canada. He picked Freedom for his base and settled in, along with his crew. The bunch of criminals and hoodlums pretty much just took over the town until the women didn't feel safe and were being forced to care for them. So, a quiet plan was hatched and spread in whispers to all the women. And, when Freedom's bells rang that Sunday morning and kept on ringing, the Belle's of Freedom were ready. Each of those men woke up, hungover from Saturday night revelries, with the bells pealing in their ears and the Belles standing over them with whatever firearm they could get their hands on. The crew was run out of town on foot and the bootlegger leader turned over to the County Sherriff.

The last time all the bells pealed together was when Freedom was threatened by a huge wildfire in the mid-1930s. Summoned by the tolling, the townspeople banded together and created a firebreak around the perimeter. Since that time, the Belle's have maintained their readiness with stories and history handed down from mother to daughter to grand-daughter, each of which passed it on to her own offspring. That's why the bells ring every day – it's their reminder to be always ready."

With a grand flourish, Jilly completed her tale and stood, hands on hips, waiting for Chloe's reaction. "So?" Jilly demanded.

"So what?" Chloe asked, bewildered.

"So... maybe Toodles meant that the Belle's are planning another rescue! A rescue of YOU!"

Chloe's face felt stiff, frozen, and ashen – like her dreams.

"Wouldn't it be AMAZING if the Belle's organized again?" Jilly continued.

Chloe's negative head shake started slow and then built into an uncontrollable quaking of her whole body. "No! No! They CAN'T!" she blurted. They were no match for Jay and his gang. Those sweet old ladies would be crushed by the thugs he ran with.

Jilly's brow furrowed as she took an involuntary step back from Chloe's vehement denial. "But.. why not? He's pushed you around long enough and has bullied the whole town!" Her words trailed off as she watched Chloe burst out the door, clutching her little plastic grocery bag.

White dominated the color palette of the town – as it was wont to do in western towns of a certain vintage. But, in keeping with its name, some free spirits had taken the town's title to heart over time, by creating sweeping vistas, western scenes and abstract paintings on several of the pristine white canvases offered by the broad walls of the barns, bars, and stores. Protected from the fierce Montana winter winds by the triple-layered windbreaks planted by the earliest settlers, the town still enjoyed a majestic and sweeping view of the plains to the east.

Chloe was briefly blinded by the blistering white of the town as she rushed from Haven's Store. However, it was only moments before she could see the splashes of color left on the towering wall of the grain elevator.

The 30' painting had been donated by one of those passing artists. While simple and slap-dash, it never-the-less evoked a deep sense of longing in Chloe. She stared up at the twirling little girl whose skirts floated up as she spread her arms and watched a pair of bluebirds cavorting above. *"What is it like to feel that free and open and carefree?"* she wondered to herself. She couldn't recall ever feeling such a thing. As if summoned by the young sprite in the painting, a breeze suddenly sprang up to peck at Chloe's hair and as if to emphasize her hopelessness, turned quickly sharp. Stepping into the lee offered by the Liberty Bar, she dug into the grocery bag and pulled out her new pack of cigarettes. Foregoing the usual tap-tap-tap to settle the tobacco, she hastily ripped off the cellophane, tore the corner and pushed out a smoke. Hands that were reluctant to release tried to gently but firmly hold the filter and work the lighter. After several tries, she relaxed slightly as the first whiffs of nicotine entered her stiff body, the chemical aftertaste lingering at the back of her tongue, like the bitter trace of her bad decisions. Taking a few drags to settle herself further, she idly contemplated the towering peaks to the west of the town which stood as if to protect the little town from the bigger world – or perhaps they were the guards to keep it from escaping. Grimacing at her own suspicious mind, she stepped back into the wind and trudged back up the hill to the decrepit trailer she called home.

Chloe heard a hollow knock on the metal front door as she slung the little plastic bag of groceries to the counter. She turned and glared at the entry, hoping it would somehow, magically, either swallow the intruder or perhaps Chloe herself. But, when a second summons came, she stomped over and flung it open.

"Chloe! Toodles mentioned she'd seen you out and about today! And then JILLY saw you in Haven's and I just KNEW it was a sign from... well, we DO have a lot of churches in Freedom so one might say we're CLOSER to the ... um... source... than most places. ANYWHO, I just KNEW it was a sign that TODAY is the DAY!" The round little gnome's enthusiastic speech was capped with the bestowal of a large baking pan presented to Chloe with a flourish.

"Um... day for what?" Chloe questioned as she stared from the pan to the old woman and back.

"Oh.. you know. The DAY for us to get acquainted" she answered as she seemed to waft through the doorway like a fresh, but strong, spring breeze. Setting the pan on the weathered and stained old door that served as a "coffee table" laid across cinder blocks, the little bubble turned, held out her arms and said, "I'm Cookie and you're Chloe and I'm SO blessed to meet a new friend!" With that, she enveloped Chloe in a soft and aromatic hug. Even though Chloe was a solid 8" taller than Cookie and should have felt awkward, she instead seemed to relax and soften in the embrace.

"Maybe it's the lilac," she thought, remembering Nana's sweet scent *"or maybe I'm just tired."* Regardless of the reason, she felt bereft when Cookie released her and then nestled into a corner of the shabby olive couch as if ready to hatch a clutch of chicks. Eying the broken lamp, full ashtrays, empty beer cans, and Chloe's swollen cheek and black eye, Cookie's eyes narrowed slightly before crinkling back up with her smiling cheeks.

"Come here and let's get acquainted" she coaxed, patting the threadbare cushion next to her. Chloe hesitated, shifting from one foot to the other.

"Um... I shouldn't really... maybe you could.... Um...." She began vaguely.

"Nonsense! I told you this is the DAY!" Cookie declared. As the old woman was obviously not budging any time soon, Chloe tentatively perched on the edge at the far end of the couch. Chewing her thumbnail, she cast glances from under her brow towards Cookie who looked steadily back, apparently waiting for Chloe to say something.

"Is that Lilac?" Chloe ventured.

Cookie grinned as if Chloe had passed a test. "My very own!" she replied.

"Nana had Lilacs." she ventured.

"Yes, I remember. All three beautiful colors – white, amethyst, and plum."

"You knew her?"

"Oh My! Yes! She was a Belle, as am I!"

"A bell?" Chloe's eyes wandered to the awful 70's wallpaper that adorned the flimsy walls and it's pattern of ships bells in faded gold.

Cookie followed her gaze and giggled in an entirely UN-old lady-like manner. "Not a 'bell' ding-ding! A Belle, b-e-l-l-e."

Chloe pondered for a moment. The only Belles she could think of were the satin-clad southern women in their hoop skirts that she'd seen on *Gone With The Wind* when she was little and watched it with Nana. Letting the thought go for the moment she looked down at her rough hands. "I don't really remember Nana having friends."

"Of course not, you were quite young and your time with her was spent mostly in her house. You'd have been too little to be taken to the Gatherings."

"Did my Mom go?" Chloe queried while wondering what "gatherings" were.

"No. She was invited and your Nana hoped she'd take her place in the Belle's as Dave was her only grandchild and so she had no other female relatives by blood. But, then your Dad died and ... well.... It just didn't work out. Your Nana never gave up hope for you, though."

Chloe looked up. "For me?"

"Well, of course, child. She was your Nana... we grandmothers are made up mostly of hope, gristle and determination" she smiled. "She said you have the same streak of ornery that Dave had – that ran in the Trudell family. The streak that caused one of your way-back ancestors to change their name to something "True" and that brought them here, as one of the founding families of Freedom, and that helped old Faith Trudell start the Belle's."

Grimacing, Chloe muttered, "What a disappointment for her – to have me prove her so wrong."

"Hm. Well, you have nothing to prove to anyone except yourself. And, I think you might find there's more inside there than you know" Cookie answered, leaning forward and tapping Chloe's heart. "For instance, I'll bet there's a wealth of love and kindness."

Chloe looked askance at the expectant old hen and gave her best "Yeah, right" face to her.

Cookie just smiled. "So, I haven't learned much about YOU," she said. "Where did you and your... um....friend.. meet?"

"Jay?" Chloe asked. Cookie nodded. "Seattle, in a dirty little bookstore. We were both sneezing from the dust." She didn't add that they'd both just run away from their homes and landed in the city and were looking for somewhere warm and dry for a few hours.

"So you felt you had at least a little in common I'll bet. But it couldn't have been just books that brought you together. Did you see something special in him?"

Unused to anyone asking anything nice about Jay, Chloe was suspicious but couldn't resist the opportunity to explain. She smiled a little as she confessed. "He was sweet. Even though we were both almost 18, he used to draw me these beautiful fairy tale castles and dragons and we'd tell stories about what we'd do if they were real. I'd always say I'd fly away and never come back and do whatever I wanted since I had a dragon. Typical kid stuff. But Jay would talk about how he'd take his dragon home and use it to save his Mom and sister and make his Dad be nice and that maybe his Dad wouldn't dare try to beat the "girl" out of him just because he liked art and reading." Recalling their early days together, how they dreamed and laughed and made plans, she turned away to hide the gathering tears.

"I knew a boy like that once. Too sweet to survive it seemed. One day he disappeared and I heard he had tried to make it in New York. Died of an overdose three years later" the faraway look in Cookie's eye slowly faded and she looked once more at Chloe. "So, how did you end up back in Freedom, bringing Jay along?"

"I used to talk about Freedom and Nana and how happy I was here before Dad.... Well, anyway, we'd been together for a while and when things started turning bad, Jay remembered that and thought it'd make a good... um... "

"Base of operations? To get yourselves 'back on your feet' so to speak?"

Chloe was pretty sure that Cookie didn't mean it the way Jay had, but she agreed. "Pretty much".

"Well, we are so glad you came home! And, I'm sorry it's taken us almost a year to meet and visit, but I want you to know that you made the right move." Cookie smiled and took Chloe's hand for a moment. "Well. I'd better toddle on home. You enjoy those brownies now, I made them special to help fatten you up, with lots of butter, frosting, and walnuts!" she declared as she pushed herself from the couch and gathered her things.

"Oh! I'm so sorry! I'm terribly allergic to nuts!" Chloe was very nearly distraught for some strange reason. "You went to all this effort for nothing!"

"Oh, I totally forgot that your Nana had mentioned that when you were little. Well, they still won't go to waste, I'm sure. Your young man, or someone, will have the munchies later and will enjoy them, even if you can't" Cookie offered as she made her way out the door and up the sidewalk, waving a casual hand over

119

her shoulder as shuffled along. "Take Care dear! See you soon!"

After Cookie left, Chloe sat on the top step of the rickety wooden front steps and lit another smoke. The conversation with her unexpected visitor had dredged up all sorts of old memories: The rainy day they met in Pike Street Market; She and Jay huddled together on a porch swing sharing their imagined futures and nightmare pasts; their first real kiss. The images flashed along, pausing here and there as she tried to recall those idyllic early days when they thought they were finally free. Before reality proved a stubborn anchor and they came to believe freedom was an illusion. Their need for food and shelter was greater than Jay's raw talent with a drawing pencil or Chloe's meager writing skills and so their passions were sacrificed. Eventually, the black cloud of their past combined with the pending storm of their present and they succumbed to the despair they'd fought so hard against. Drugs were not only an easy escape but also became a quick source of income.

Sometimes at night, Chloe would like awake and watch Jay. In his sleeping face, she saw traces, still, of that sweet boy she'd first fallen for. But, those traces were being slowly eroded like the surrounding plains were scoured by the never-ending wind, and she feared that soon they'd both lose the last vestiges of their better selves. But, she could see no way to stop the destruction.

Frustrated, restless and scared, Chloe suddenly crushed out her cigarette and rising, stomped into the trailer to distract herself with some housework. After picking up the broken pieces of lamp, emptying ashtrays and cleaning up the garbage and detritus from last night's party, she decided to call up Jilly and apologize for running out on her that morning.

It startled her to hear Jilly's voice as soon as she put the phone to her ear, she hadn't even heard it ring once on the other end. "Chloe! Are you ok? You ran out so fast, I was afraid something was wrong."

"Hey, Jilly. No, I'm fine. I just... well... you know I don't really like talking about Jay and me and I don't understand why everyone seems to think I need "rescued". Geez, it's been the recurring theme today! But, anyway, I just wanted to say Sorry for running out so fast."

"It's ok. I'm glad nothing's wrong. Oh, by the way... I'm supposed to give you a message."

"From who?"

"Granny. I don't know exactly what she's trying to say, but she said to tell you 'Not to ignore Hope's knock.' She can be a little kooky, you know."

Chloe had met Jilly's Grandmother once, and 'kooky' seemed the least of the descriptions she'd use for the large woman who wore glittery silver moon boots and a floppy leather hat all year and added a moth-eaten fur coat for winter. She had grabbed Chloe the first time they met and nearly smothered her with a bear hug. Then, pushing her back, had bellowed "Little Chloe Trudell!" while gripping Chloe's jaw and turning her head side to side. "Mmhmm.... you have that stubborn Trudell jaw. Your Nana always called it her 'German jaw' although there wasn't a drop of German in THAT Norwegian package. 'Course, I see your mama too... you're beautiful green eyes fairly shout her shabby Irish clan."

Chloe had just opened her mouth to take offense at the "shabby" used so casually when the fleshy face smiled and transformed the oddly mannish woman into a radiant angel. Love, joy, and peace all seemed to emanate from that suddenly dazzling face, hinting at the promise of Paradise. "Ah.. but I see the mark of God on you. He has great plans for you, Chloe." With that bizarre pronouncement, the strange creature had sailed off to her next encounter.

"Speaking of kooky, I met Cookie today... seems like all the women in Freedom are a little crazy." Chloe observed.

"Oh! I love Cookie! She always smells so divine. You know where she lives, right?" Jilly asked.

"No. We didn't talk about her much."

"You know that run-down old Victorian place, just out of town with the HUGE gardens all around it? That's hers... I guess her family has always been big into flowers and herbs and stuff."

"Why don't I remember all these old women from when we were little?" Chloe wondered.

"Well, they weren't OLD then, silly!"

"Yes, I guess you're right," Chloe admitted.

"Hey.. I gotta run. I'm working at the Liberty tonight & need to get ready. But I'm glad you called!" Jilly said.

"Ok, I should go too. Talk to you later." Chloe agreed. Hitting the "End" button, she dropped into the overstuffed brown armchair and scooched around until she was as comfortable as possible with all the lumps and holes. Staring at the screen on the phone, she aimlessly clicked around until some old photos of her and Jay came up. Slowly swiping through the pictures, she suddenly stopped and studied one closely. Jay, with his soft black curls drooping over his eyes as he focused intently on a drawing, his whole body hunched over the drawing pad on his pulled-up knees and left arm curled around the pad, pencil clutched in his right. She used to sit and watch him for hours as his whole being riveted on trying to get the vision in his head down on paper. Then, suddenly, he'd look up at her and she'd be able to see in his eyes his frustration, or rarely, his triumph. He'd been so optimistic that his life could be better than what his childhood had shown. That all he needed do was work hard enough and dream big enough. In the frozen moment she could still clearly see his hope, his gentleness, his un-calloused heart. In the Before.

Suddenly she was jerked back to the After – the Present – by the slamming of car doors and loud voices hurtling invectives through the air. Peeking through the curtain's edge, she saw the trio of rusted old Chevy, Honda and Pontiac disgorging their passengers like blisters weeping infection. She stood as boots stomped up the steps and the door was flung wide. "CHLOE!!" came the bellow. "Where the HELL...." Trailed off as he spotted her standing in the gloom. "Get me a God-damn beer!!

"We're out..." she started to explain timidly.

"They're in the fucking car." He threw at her as he bulled his way past and crashed to the couch. Chloe threaded her way through the incoming tide of his sycophants and pulled the case of Rainier from the hatchback of the bilious Honda. Lugging it inside, she wrestled it to the counter and opened the end of the cardboard box. Pulling out cans, she started handing them out to the refuse crowding the small space, suddenly noticing the toxic combination of smells. Rancid body odor, the sickly sweet taste of old cigarette smoke, and car grease combined with the yeast of fresh beer to eliminate the lingering traces of lilac and cleansers. Carefully perching on the arm of the couch near Jay, she tried to quietly figure out why they were back so soon.

"I'm glad to see you" she started, laying a cautious hand on his arm, "but I didn't expect you back so quickly."

Jay's scowl deepened. "We got the product no problem in Glasgow. But, when we got close to the interstate down by Butte, the cops were everywhere. Then we got a message from our contact and he said they had a BOLO out for our cars on the interstate. So, we decided to get our asses back here and lay low for a few days. Pisses me off! How'd they know we were coming through?"

"It's ok. It'll blow over. You'll get the shipment through." Chloe tried to reassure him, but knew her heart wasn't in it tonight. Jay jerked away & lurched upright, stomping over to replace the beer he'd guzzled.

"Just don't get it.... How the HELL..." he muttered to himself as he opened the fresh brew. Chloe followed him into the minuscule kitchen area and offered a tentative smile as she leaned beside him against the chipped press-board counter and opened a beer of her own.

"Do you remember when we first met?" she asked as she looked down at the can in her hand.

Obviously confused and irritated at the odd question, Jay snapped back "What? What the hell does that have to do with anything?"

"I was just thinking today about all the plans we had then. You were such an amazing artist... I was thinking that maybe we gave up on our dreams too soon....." she trailed off as she noticed his expression. His face had gone solid as if a barrier of steel had suddenly grown under his skin. He grabbed her upper arm in a tight, almost painful grip.

"Don't EVER bring that up. Not EVER. Only the weak wish for something they'll never have. Art, dreams, future plans – those are for the stupid, whining weaklings out there!" He jabbed his cigarette toward the door, slopping the beer he still held in the same hand. Throwing her arm away, he turned and lumbered back to the couch, angrily flinging himself onto the worn cushions. Chloe bit her lip and fought to keep the tears at bay. One thing she had learned with absolute certainty – you never showed tears or weakness to this crowd. They would pounce like a band of jackals.

As the night progressed, Jay's frustration and anger grew and the entire crew was drinking heavily as the pot smoke grew thick. Knowing the unpredictability of Jay and his followers when such forces as these combined, and wanting to keep her wits about her, Chloe drank sparingly and simply passed the joint when it came by. At some point in the evening, as the marijuana started to take effect, the crew discovered the brownies and the morsels started disappearing steadily. An aging, but bold, red-headed woman turned on her music – a heavy, thumping, rage filling the room. But, as the group seemed inclined to do nothing more than sulk for the night, Chloe eventually slipped away to the bedroom. Expecting the noise to continue well into the morning hours, she leaned against the headboard and lit a new cigarette. As she lay listening to the thump from the front room, she let her mind again turn to the past, but it didn't seem to settle on any one memory – simply jumping from remembered feeling to mental picture to emotional aches, she eventually crushed out the butt and closed her eyes, trying NOT to think.

Hours later, she awoke with a sense of expectation mixed with uneasiness. Jay lay beside her, having fallen onto the mottled blue comforter at some unknown point. His curly forelock lay limply across his brow while a sliver of saliva slipped from his slightly parted lips onto the threadbare flannel pillowcase. Sitting up, she listened for whatever had awakened her. With the ivory rivulets of sunrise steadily running across the floor like the promise of a slow, but cleansing, flood, she realized that it was eerily silent in the trailer. Slipping down the hallway, she quietly peered into the gloom of the living room. Most of the crew was passed out in chairs, on the floor or on the couch. They seemed to be sleeping heavily as she stood and surveyed the wreckage. Walking to the window, she glanced out at the butter-colored morning and pondered whether to try and sleep more or if she should just sit on the stoop with her morning nicotine. A sudden, but timid, knock at the front door made her jump and she looked around quickly at the sleeping bodies, but they didn't even twitch at the sound. Filled with trepidation, she tiptoed over the still forms and cracked the door, peering out with one eye to see who might be so brave as to risk Jay's wrath. A frown creased her brow as she slowly opened the door further and then stepped out to look up and down the street. No one seemed to be in view, but the small brown paper handle bag sitting on the third step proved she hadn't imagined the sound.

As she bent to cautiously pick up the package, she had the strange sensation of being watched, but after another careful look around and still not seeing anyone, she backed into the house and carefully latched the door. Standing in the murky gloom, brightened only by the narrow window in the door, she squinted into the bag. Confused, she pulled out a handful of zip-ties, typically used as extremely strong bands to hold items such as cords, pipes, etc., together. Under the ties, was a folded paper and several glossy tri-fold brochures. A glance at the latter showed they were all for in-house treatment centers for drug and alcohol abuse. Opening the note, she read:

Freedom is in your hands, but YOU must decide. Will you set yourself – and Jay – free? Or will you continue to live in bondage to your addictions? You have several choices: A. You can stay and lose your chance at a new life. 2. You can simply walk out now and leave the others to continue their destruction while you start that new life. Or, 3. You can choose to help the whole town and Jay, by restraining him and the others and giving them a chance to not only face Justice, but to also accept responsibility and also be given the chance to start new lives.

Following this challenge, was a phone number with "Sherriff Connell". Chloe let the paper fall back into the bag as she struggled with her emotions. Wasn't it a betrayal of her love for Jay to walk out? And even more so to turn him in? But, wasn't it also a betrayal of herself to continue down the path she was on? Chewing her lip, she stood indecisively. Finally, after several minutes, she made her decision.

-------------   --------------------   ----------
----------   -----------------   -----------

Across the street, Sherriff Joyce Connell stood in the hidden lee of the old barn, watching the tired mobile home. Behind her, Cookie and Toodles stood together, both seemingly certain of the outcome. The Sherriff had told them NOT to come, but there they were when she arrived in the dark, several hours earlier, already watching the quiet neighborhood. She cautioned them that things didn't always go the way one wanted – she knew that better than most – and that they shouldn't get their hopes up. Remembering her own escape many years earlier and the losses she'd suffered, made her sympathetic to the girl's predicament, but it also made her wary of trusting someone so bruised and confused. And so, with the full squad at the ready, she prepared to take the matter into the hands of the Law, should Chloe take the easy way out. As the minutes passed and lengthened, she began to ready herself. As she started to motion to her deputies, she felt a vibration. Her phone was ringing.

BAGGAGE

"How Deep?" the disembodied voice floated up from the inky depths as metal struck dirt.

"Six feet by six feet by three feet" I replied.

"Why so deep? He's barely grown!"

"Because I want to bury his baggage with him."

"Baggage?" the voice exclaimed as it climbed out of the hole. "How can a horse have baggage?"

"The baggage that left a six-month-old colt tied to a tree all day in wolf country" I replied just before I pulled the trigger.

Jeff playing harmonica by fire in Montana

Jeff & Sara with Josie – lunch on the trail

Jeff, Sara & Josie at Cached Lake

Packing a camp out of Fly Basin

Packing up the East Fork of Pine Creek

Made in the USA
Columbia, SC
17 July 2021

41941940R00081